'Fit like, Skipper?'

A collection of North-east tales and poems

by PETER BUCHAN

1985

ABERDEEN JOURNALS LIMITED

ISBN 0 9510642 1 5

ACKNOWLEDGEMENTS

We are grateful to the following contributors for their help in compiling the collection of pictures in this book: Peter Bruce (Buckie), Jim Stephen (Boddam), S. R. Services (Peterhead), Mrs M. Buchan, Mr & Mrs F. Hurry, and Peter Forman, all of Peterhead.

Printed in Great Britain
by W. M. Bett Ltd, Tillicoultry

Contents

Foreword

Peter Buchan, born into a Peterhead fisher family, a man who has spent most of his life at sea or working in the harbour area, writes from an intimate knowledge of his subject as only an insider can do. He knows, often from bitter experience, whereof he speaks.

For long, the fishers here in the North-east have been almost a race apart, their customs, their traditions, their superstitions, their very way of life a mystery to the rest of us. Mr Buchan lets us into that world.

Without being in the least mawkish – his highly original writing style is always spiced with humour – he harks back to a time when poverty made brothers of all men and when community spirit had a meaning because it was the only way people could survive.

He has recaptured the way our forefathers lived and brought these long-dead men and women to life again in his stories. A storyteller of the calibre of Peter Buchan comes but rarely and it is sobering to realise how much would have been lost had he not been compelled to put pen to paper.

The Doric is his language and he writes it the way he speaks it, which is not just a talent given to everyone. His fund of yarns – the sceptical may call them tall tales – is seemingly inexhaustible and if the facts are sometimes embellished, are they not all the better for being so?

His collection of poems, 'Mount Pleasant', is now in its sixth edition; the publication of this selection of his prose writings and some of his poems will be welcomed by the many readers of his articles in the *Evening Express*.

There is much that is based on fact, much on Mr Buchan's own experiences, but one also has to remember that Mr Buchan is strong on imagination.

Peter Oxo, as he is known in Peterhead, where Buchans are ten-a-penny and tee-names are used to distinguish one from the other, has his fellow man taped. And that's not always comfortable.

Those piercing blue eyes – a seaman's eyes for scanning distant horizons – seem to have the power to bore right into your soul and sum you up, not always favourably. That quizzical grin unsettles.

He doesn't miss much, he with the air of the wise elder statesman. And then there's that awe-inspiring memory which is a powerful ally.

His life would indeed have been different had his father lived. It was to have been university and a good job on land. The sea gave a poor return in those days. But when his father died, the sea it had to be and Peter Buchan characteristically made the most of it.

From his home, 'Mount Pleasant', an early 18th century house overlooking the vast expanse of Peterhead bay with its constant to-ing and fro-ing of traffic, Mr Buchan, now retired, concentrates on his writing.

With his dry humour and biting wit, he is adept at recording people's quirks and foibles. His character studies are masterly.

In the 'Turk', the skipper hero of some of his more highly coloured tales, he has created a 'Para Handy' character.

It has to be said that there are those of delicate sensibilities who may grimace at a certain earthy, nay salty quality which strays into his writing. Peter Buchan has never held back from telling it like it is. Take it or leave it.

Forgive him for his insight into human nature, his perception of man's failings and weaknesses, his compassion for the underdog, his inimitable style and most of all for his writing. But then the man is a poet.

Sheila Hamilton

1

Tall tales of the old salts

In the halcyon days of my youth an old Russian cannon from the Crimean War stood in Harbour Street with its great muzzle pointing towards the Skerry.

The underside of the massive barrel was pitted by the salty atmosphere but its top was as smooth as glass, polished by the doups of generations of bairns who had sat astride it. The old relic was removed to help the war effort in the 1940s, but the seats are still there. These old seats were the recognised meeting place for the old salts and ancient mariners of the locality, for in those days there was neither radio nor TV to while away the hours of retirement.

Consequently a proper 'Parliament' foregathered around the seats in the afternoons and evenings if the weather was good and many a wonderful tale was told, tales of whaling days, tales of the hellish life in the trenches of Flanders, for the old boys were not all fishermen, tales of the mine-sweepers and the Dover Patrol and tales of every imaginable sort.

One thing is for sure – these old codgers caught far more herring and fish around the seats than they ever did at sea!

For a long time I had the impression that the fishing boats of their day had been very big boats to carry such shots of fish until I realised that among these ancients there were several practised liars whose mendacity even I have never managed to equal – and that's saying something!

I soon learned that any member of that illustrious gathering who was without a nickname was bound to be an incomer.

I must have been a proper nuisance to Simon McLeod, a cooper who hailed from Tobermory, and John Skinner, from Balintore, for every time I met them I would speir 'Far div 'ee come fae?' simply for the joy of hearing the Highland lilt as they pronounced the names of their birthplaces.

Then there was 'Wansie', a local cooper with a huge moustache, from which protruded a beautiful amber cigarette holder presented to him by Lord Kitchener after the battle of Tel-el-Kebir.

Apparently Kitchener had planned to surprise the enemy by making an overnight forced march across the desert sands, but in the course of this manoeuvre he had got himself hopelessly lost. In despair he brought his army to a halt, with one hand, just as John Wayne does on the screen.

It was a moment for split second decision so he barked the order 'Go and find Wansie!'

Wansie was immediately brought from the rear of the column, where he had been peelin' tatties, to the forefront, where, steering by the stars he led the British Army to glorious victory.

His medal for this stupendous feat had perished in the desert heat, but the cigarette holder had survived. What a man! Very few could peel tatties and march at the same time!

When at a later date I was asked to name, in order of importance, the three greatest navigators of all time, I wrote – Wansie, Nancy's Peter and Beetlies Daavit, whereupon I was banished from the classroom in disgrace!

This only served to prove that certain schoolteachers can be very ignorant indeed!

One of my favourite friends was Jimmy Buchan, known to all the community as 'Trappin'. A little wee mannie always spick and span, he lived in Hay's Close where a rickle of old tenements served to accommodate an unbelieveable number of folk.

When I asked him one day 'Foo mony folk bides in that close, Jimmy?' he replied, 'Och! A gey lot, my loon! We jist bide mix-max an' pairt the bairns at the New 'Ear!'

It would have been most improper of me to ask him how he got his by-name, so I had to inquire elsewhere and it was thus-wise – the old time fishermen wore a fantastic amount of clothing. To begin with, every one had a pair of hand knitted drawers, which could vary in colour from shocking pink to emerald green.

The upper part of the body was clad in a flannel shirt or 'linner', surmounted by a 'wincey' sark which in turn was covered by a 'frock', a long jersey which reached below the hips and was always of five-ply navy blue Seafield worsit!

The galluses which supported the heavy trousers were worn above the frock whose lower part was always out of sight beneath the breeks. These same galluses would have made an adequate mooring for the QE2.

If it was an airish mornin' they would don an ordinary ganjie forbye! But now I must let you in on an awful secret! Between their drawers and their breeks they wore 'drawers covers' which were nothing more or less than a pair of thin white cotton pants which were fastened round the wearer's ankles with lengths of tape. It was mandatory that this tape be tied in a neat little bow or 'doss'.

Jimmy, in his own thrawn manner, refused to accept the modern word 'tape' and insisted on the old term 'trapping'. So for the remainder of his days he was 'Trappin'.

Trappin was one of the remarkable breed who go to sea alone in small boats. Foolhardy? A wee bittie, maybe. Fearless? Aye! Surely!

He would leave port at dawn in his 18 foot sail boatie, his provisions being fourpence worth of butter cookies and a cutter o' Fuskie, and his range was wide, indeed, especially if he could get a seine-netter to tow him 'as far as Cruden Skares or the Slains Buss'!

I'm thinking now of one lovely summer morning during my first year at sea when we found old Trappin in his boatie at Rattray Head. He was fast asleep in the bottom of the boat snugly wrapped in the sail, and when I boarded his vessel and woke him up he wisna neen suited!

But a shallie o' tay from our taypot mollified him and he went on his way rejoicing. He had been at sea for twenty-six hours!

One particularly coorse day he was caught in the fearsome tide rip which makes the North Head at Peterhead such a terrifying place. He was battling with wind and tide to bring his boatie to harbour when disaster struck.

The spar which carries the sail (i.e., the yard) broke, so Trappin was helpless.

Anxious watchers on shore alerted the lifeboat which was quickly on the scene to find him trying his utmost to mend the broken yard. The gallant lifeboat coxswain manoeuvred his craft alongside the casualty ready to snatch the luckless sailor from a watery grave, only to be roundly berated by the irate Trappin with the question, 'Fit on earth are ye deein' oot here on a day like this? Ye should hae mair sense, man!'

Thus the worthies who were such an important feature of my impressionable boyhood. As I have already said, the seats remain to this day, but the old men have passed on.

Friendship from a pain in the neck

The words 'Shipmate' and 'Friend' are not necessarily synonymous! I have often seen shipmates who just managed to tolerate each other and I have seen shipmates who simply hated each other's guts for no apparent reason.

And then there are shipmates between whom there appears to be a natural bond of sincere friendship which lasts for many years, but having said that, let's not forget the friendships which can blossom between the most 'unsuitable' partners, folk who have absolutely nothing in common.

Once upon a time I had such a friendship with a shipmate whom I shall call John – not his real name.

I was young enough to run rings round him – of this he was daily reminded – and still we were friends. He was the most contermashious divvle I have ever sailed with, having an inordinate passion for the truth and nothing but the truth!

To him a spade was a spade and in no way would he accept my suggestion that it could be classed as a 'thing for howkin' holes'. When I put forward the idea that the truth is not always required I was a heretic, a man without principle, without solid foundation, to be classed with those who patch their drawers wi' velvet! And still, man, still we were friends.

I think it all started when John developed, on the back of his neck, a plook like a half egg, a hideous mass of corruption wi' a gut as thick as a pencil. The poor man couldn't see the thing at all and when he tried to ficher wi' the plook on his own he simply aggravated it.

So I offered to assist, having suffered greatly myself with a like affliction. With Lysol and hot water for the outside and a vile mixture of Epsom salts and Cream o' Tartar for the inside coupled with a heap o' patience for both sides the mountain was reduced to a plain and all was well!

From that time onward we became the best of pals. On the rare occasions when he threatened to become a wee bittie obstreperous I simply had to hint that in future he would 'squeeze his ain plooks', then he would be as meek as a lamb.

In appearance John was naething forbye. He was short and stout so much so that when he donned his oilskin frock he resembled a herrin' barrel wi' little feeties on't. His bonnet was always dead flat on his head and my gentle hint that a five-degree tilt might enhance his appearance brought the sharp retort that he had no time for the Nelson touch. If that had been in his mind he 'would ha' bocht a bonnet wi' the snoot at the side'!

John's normal voice was softer and gentler than any womans' but when he sang he could gar yer taes curl! He had a glorious bass voice which reverberated like a teem cask, a gift which drew many an admiring glance in the Deneside Chapel in Yarmouth where the locals 'couldn't get a seat for Scotties' unless they were half-an-hour early. Ye'll mind, the Kirk wi' the picter-hoose seats!

Such was John, a mixter of soft voice and ill naitur', a blend of coorseness and kindliness, a man whose strongest expletive was 'Ooh me! Ooh me!'

He had started his working life as a cooper but after a few years at his trade he had forsaken it for the sea, to serve for several years as a trawler cook. The fact that he had been cook in the same vessel under the same skipper for seven years was a great testimonial, for good cooks are worth their weight in gold!

John, according to John, was worth at least that for wasn't he the finest cook that ivver steered a pot?

His skipper was one of the top-notchers, a hard man in a hard world. The shippie was a common five eight Aiberdeen trawler and as such she had no shelter decks whatsoever. The crew had to tak' their shak' on an open deck whatever the weather.

I have never forgotten John's account of one wild stormy day away to the east of the Shetlands. Several trawlers had been fishing in close company but one-by-one they had knocked off because of the atroeious weather.

John's skipper as usual, was last to give in and when he did finally give the order to heave up, the crew of seasoned veterans had grave doubts whether or not this could be done without loss of life, but the net, with a bumper haul was brought safely aboard. The deckies were not too pleased at seeing the 'ponds' brimming with fish because they wouldn't get off the deck till the fish were gutted and it really wasn't a day for men to be on deck at all.

The skipper asked John to go forrard and lend a hand and this he did willingly only to be told by the Mate 'look here cookie! When ye're on deck ye'll dee fit I tell ye, so fin the skipper's nae lookin', ye'll shovel fish ower the side!

'We want to get below afore dark, but watch that the mannie disna see fit ye're deein!' So John busied himself with a shovel.

Now on such a day a drifter would have had her great mizzen sail set, the wheel lashed in the mid-ships position and with the engine at slow ahead she would have lain head to wind more or less looking after herself. But it was the custom in trawlers to let the ship lie broadside on to wind and sea until the weather abated. Great green seas would come crashing on board filling the decks waist deep in a torrent.

I have never been in a trawler but I can well imagine that to work fish on an open deck in such conditions must have been sheer Hell!

The skipper in his lofty eyrie in the wheel-house kept a sharp look-out to windward and when he saw a particularly nasty 'lump o' water' coming he would yell 'Hud on lads, hud on!' whereupon every man would grab for some immovable fixture and hang on for dear life until the worst was past.

If bad language could have quelled the seas there would have been a flat clam but the sea is stone deaf to epithets.

Roughly half of the fish had been gutted when a most peculiar incident took place. The deckie nearest to John suddenly 'gid wrang in 'is mind'. Something in the poor chap's brain snapped and casting his knife into the sea he seized the rigging of the foremast and hoisted himself onto the top-rail, i.e. the top of the bulwark. There he stood erect before setting out on a sort of tight-rope walk along the rail right into the stern of the ship where he squatted for a few moments with his back to the crutch of the mizzen boom, looking steadfastly into the eye of the wind.

Then, erect again, he retraced his steps along the same impossible path back to the fore-mast where his awe-struck shipmates seized him and hustled him below. There he remained under supervision until the proper authorities took charge of him in his home port.

No sooner had his shipmates got him below when one almighty sea came sweeping aboard. It lifted every moveable thing in its path – fish, baskets, pond-boards, the lot, and tossed them contemptuously over the lee side. Had the crew been there, their chances of survival had been slim indeed.

When John had finished his story he was very close to tears. 'Tell me this,' he said, 'Fit wye wis't that nae wan drap o' water came in ower the rail as lang as he wis on't?' Alas! I could not answer.

That finished the trip, for the skipper immediately set course for home. It was also the finish for John as far as trawling was concerned. He had witnessed the impossible and he didna like it! In fact he had seen the Supernatural and he was scared stiff!

It's almost thirty years now since John passed on. It's at least forty years since he told me the tale and I think the incident took place some ten or twelve years before that. Say fifty-odd years ago.

Never once have I doubted his word but I have yet to come up with an answer to his question – 'Fit wye?'

Chasing herring in Stornoway

During the summer of 1934 I was a young lad on our family boat *Sparkling Star* a 40-footer, built by John Stephen of Macduff.

At that time there was quite a fleet of similar boats, mostly in the Moray Firth, built for skippers who had been obliged to get rid of their uneconomical steam drifters. Most of these skippers had been herring fishermen all their days and had retained their herring nets for use in their new craft, so that particular summer there were several such craft fishing from Stornoway.

And why Stornoway? Simply because the herring shoals at Stornoway are usually near the coast, very handy for such small boats. And why 40 feet? Because the law decreed that on certain parts of the Scottish coast boats of under 40 feet were allowed to use the seine net inside the three mile limit.

So these skippers were actually trying to make dual-purpose vessels out of boats which were too small for that. They were never meant to be herring boats and gradually they forsook the herring fishing to concentrate on the seine-net. But during the summer which concerns our story, Stornoway was full of them, BCK and BF. We were the only PD.

Boys! That was a disastrous summer! Scarcely a herrin' could be found anywhere. It was the same all around the coast, a proper famine. Had there been herrin' elsewhere we would have shifted but there was no inducement to move so we stuck it out for several weeks for absolutely nothing.

As a young feel loon I was quite happy with my ten bob (50p) on Saturday. With that I could get all the fags and ice-cream I wanted, Player's being only a shilling (5p) for twenty, but had I been a married man wi' bairns, the situation would have been grim indeed.

I have a vivid memory of one particular Monday morning. The harbour at Bayhead was crammed with small craft, their crews all busy making the nets ready for sea. There was an air of bustle and good humour about the place with old veterans telling the loons, 'Watch 'ee yer wark an' I'll watch the pier.

If a quine worth lookin' at comes along, I'll tell ye!'

Paraffin men were busy with their deliveries and all kinds of message boys were crossing and recrossing the boats when suddenly all activity ceased and there fell on the scene a fearsome hush!

A Post Office boy had appeared on the quay with a bright coloured envelope in his hand. Telegram for somebody! Certain disaster!

It was obvious that the boy was looking for a certain boat for he scanned every tier closely as he moved slowly along the quay glancing now and then at the envelope. Countless eyes followed his path and many a man heaved a sigh of relief when the boy passed him by!

The tension was almost unbearable for telegrams were usually bearers of calamitous tidings. Sure as death it had to be the very last boat that he boarded with every eye fixed on him. The recipient opened the envelope with trembling fingers then threw his bonnet in the air yelling, 'Twins, twa quines, b' Goad!' And suddenly everybody was happy! Oh! what a beautiful mornin'!

Later that week we were amazed to see on the quay ten men, in identical new suits and bonnets, led by a mannie in a paddy hat.

They too were scanning the fleet for a certain boat and great was our surprise when the boat turned out to be ours!

Paddy-Hat explained that these men were the crew of the *Ocean Princess*, an Aberdeen 'liner' which had grounded during the night near the little village of Ness. The crew had rowed ashore, to be transported to Stornoway where the British Sailors' Society had looked after them and kitted them out. Hence the new suits!

Now they were desirous of returning to the wreck to see if she could be salvaged. Since they were Aiberdeen men they would like a Peterhead boatie to act as ferry-boat. If we undertook to do the job we would be handsomely paid! Indeed we would get 'saxteen powen'! Nae bother. For that kind of money we would take them to the Flannan Isles!

It transpired that the *Ocean Princess* had been heading for Stornoway to procure herring bait before proceeding to distant fishing grounds such as St Kilda or Rockall or Faroe where she would work her long-lines for about a fortnight before returning to her home port. This was common practice with the Aberdeen line boats.

On the way to the wreck some twenty miles distant it was chance aboot for tay because our little foc'sle was designed for six and we now had sixteen on board. But that was to be a short-lived inconvenience for we'd soon be putting these chaps back aboard their own vessel.

Imagine then our astonishment when we found the *Ocean Princess* afloat with another Aberdeen liner, the *Craigcoilleach*, standing by to render assistance. The casualty had been taken over by two villagers from Ness and in no way would they allow any member of the crew to step aboard! In this they were within their legal rights. Laws of salvage, you see!

It had so happened that the two 'Hielan'men' had boarded the wreck to investigate the situation. Of course, there were some charitable people who said: 'Oh aye! We've heard that before! The ship had been provisioned in Aberdeen the day before with stores for ten or twelve men for three weeks, plus a fine big locker packed with bond (tobacco and spirits). She was certainly worth investigating! Jealousy is to be found everywhere.

I heard later that the two chaps had just gone below to see if there was water in the ship when there came a fearsome rummle like an earthquake! In terror they rushed back on deck to find that the ship had slid off the rock and was now afloat and in no immediate danger of sinking. The heroes had enough 'mither wit' to realise that the prize was theirs!

In the off-shore wind the *Ocean Princess* drifted away clear of the land and she was lying fine and handy when the *Craigcoilleach* came along. The prize crew engaged this new arrival to tow them to Stornoway. I doubt if our little boat could have done the job.

We could see that the casualty's rudder was jammed hard to starboard but our offer to act as a rudder during the tow was refused. So all we could do was to take our passengers back to Stornoway.

Next morning the tow arrived in Stornoway where she was successfully beached and repaired.

The two locals were very handsomely rewarded by the courts which settle salvage questions. The amount of the award I have forgotten but I can well remember for those times it was a colossal sum.

It may surprise you to know that only one of these lucky lads was a local. The other was a Peterhead man who had made his home there. Strangè how Bluemogganers manage to put in an appearance when there's 'something to be gotten!'

Fog at high water was always a break

'One gun for the Apparatus, two guns for the Lifeboat!' That was a code which I learned at a very tender age for I was born and brought up about 100 yards from the Lifeboat Shed.

Of course they weren't really guns, but rockets or 'maroons', yet to this day its aye the 'Lifeboat guns'. These guns were heard a great deal oftener in my youth than they are today, not so much because of ships in difficulty through stress of weather, but because of ships grounded in fog. 'A ship ashore!'

Over the past thirty years fog has lost a lot of its terror. Sophisticated electronic devices – echo-sounders, Decca Navigators and radar have proved invaluable to fishermen who can now tell at a glance their exact position, the depth of water below the keel, and the presence, if any, of other ships in the vicinity not forgetting the precise distance of land! No surprise then that so few craft are stranded because of fog.

But when I was a young fisherman there were no such devices and going to sea in foggy weather could be a great strain on the nerves. Fog can play havoc with one's sense of judgment. There are times when a gull sitting on the sea can assume the proportions of a destroyer, and there are times when a streak of soot or the wake from a passing ship can be easily mistaken for rocks.

A few days of seeking the shore in 'smore thick' conditions and your 'een 'll be like pipe-lids! Your lugs will be on the alert listenin', listenin' for the foghorn or the horns of other vessels and before the week's oot ye'll be like a rag!'

Now here's a strange thing! Fog has an uncanny habit of lifting at high-water! The reason why is beyond me but nevertheless it is a fact. Those exalted beings who study depressions and fronts (cold or warm) along with swirls of cloud and satellite pictures will naturally pooh-pooh this statement, but jist like ither folk they dinna ken aathing!

For fifty years I've watched this phenomenon, if that be the proper word, and I can say, along with countless others of my generation that 'if the fog disna lift at high-water ye may as weel ging hame'!

Of course it doesn't always happen but it happens a great deal oftener than not! Far too often for coincidence, but then a race which has been born into the age of electronics will probably never notice such a thing.

I'm thinking now of a particularly foggy morning in the Thirties. The crews of the inshore boaties were pacing back and fore in the old fishmarket at Peterhead waiting to see if the fog would lift. The 'Boddan Coo' (Buchan Ness Horn) had been roarin' the hale nicht and was still roarin'. To go to sea in such a fog was unthinkable so we would 'hing on' till high-water and, if it didna clear, we would ging hame. High-water came but there was no change in the weather so the bourachie o' fishers dispersed.

On the way home I was accompanied by a friend called Philip Cowe who bade in Merchant Street. 'This is the holiday' says he 'An' my twa quines is for Aiberdeen on the first bus. What a price to pey for a fare! Three and ninepence return! It's nae mowse! I'll be in fine time to mak' their tay afore they rise.'

Now 'Cowie' is a Moray Firth name, awa up aboot Buckie somewye, but 'Cowe' is a name fae the Broch to Rattray Heid. It canna hae onything t' dae wi' cattle or the name wid ha' been 'Coo'. According to Hamewith, 'Cowe' means 'the branch or twig of a wayside shrub'. Still, that is by the way.

Philip had just got the kettle bilin' when he heard the milk cairt at the door. Like countless others in the toon, he had 'folk bidin' up the stair' so he wid hae t' watch that he didna tak' the wrang milk!

When Philip got to the door the milkman, a stand-in for the usual man, was in the act of putting two separate lots of milk on the step, so, pointing to the right-hand lot Philip says cheerfully 'Zat Cowe's milk?'

The stooping milkman slowly raised himself an' dichtit the dreep fae his nose, then he launched into a proper tirade.

'No! It's nae cow's milk, ye great dytit fisher feel! I'm jist this meenit hame fae the Sahara. I've been up aaa nicht milkin' camels! I'll gie ye cow's milk! Some o' you fisher chiels disna ken dirt fae chappit dates!'

Philip grabbed a bottle an' bolted into the hoose!

Next time that fog forced us to call off our day's fishing he says 'Peter, I'm nae gaun hame till the milkman's by'!

Now, for those who insist that there's nothing in a name, let me resurrect a tale from the distant days of my youth. It would appear that a Moray Firth fisherman with a Moray Firth name gave up the sea to start a sweetie shoppie.

Proud of his new premises, he painted in bold letters above the door his name, R. Slater, then spent the rest of his days wondering how and why he had acquired the nickname Heid First!

Suntie Claas couldnae beat this present!

It was the last week in November and the East Anglian fishing was in its final stages.

The herring shoals had left their normal haunts among the tide-swept sand banks off the Norfolk coast and had moved elsewhere. This surprised nobody because this was an occurrence which had varied very little for many generations if not for centuries.

The end of November was the time when the Scots in their thousands would leave for home; indeed quite a few boats had already sailed and most of the remaining skippers were 'on the pirr'.

Of course some of the real die-hards would stick it out for a while and try the notoriously coorse fishing grounds at Sandettie off the French coast, but none of them would outlast Christmas Charlie from Cairnbulg who for many years had made it his rule never to leave Yarmouth before Christmas, hence his nickname.

His boat was a relic of the days of sail and altho' she had been fitted with a diesel engine, only a stout heart would have gone to Yarmouth in her at all, let alone stay till Christmas!

Well now, twas Saturday and most skippers were advising their crews 'I dinna think we'll be here anither week-end. We'll try't the first o' the week an' if there's nae herrin' we'll just leave fae the sea, so ye'd better buy your presents the day! Ye'll get a sub if ye need it!' Maist o' the lads nott a sub.

Some lucky crews who had been fortunate enough to run to Ijmuiden in Holland with a big shot would have had their presents bought long ago – a bonny tray wi' win'mills on't for the wife, or a pair o' widden clogs for the bairn. But most of the fishers would have to do their shopping in Yarmouth and since there were several thousands of them, to say nothing of the guttin' quines and the coopers, the local shops did very well indeed and the rock factory had to work overtime.

There was a certain mystique about the Yarmouth present! An identical gift from Aberdeen could not possibly be half as good, and a 'stalk' (not a 'stick') of Yarmouth Rock could far surpass anything in the candy shoppies at hame.

Boys, how the fisher bairns smelt of peppermint in December!

And wasn't it wonderful when Da sent hame a 'boxie' maybe halfway through the season? A boxie wi some rock, twa-three aipples an' pomegranates! I'm sure the trees in Eden never bore sweeter fruit!

This reminds me of the true story of the Sunday School class whose earnest teacher asked that every pupil who wished to go to Heaven should raise a hand. Every hand save one shot up!

The startled teacher, gazing kindly at the young heretic asked in a whisper 'Fits adee, my loon? Fit wye div 'ee nae want t' ging't Heaven?'

''Cos I hinna gotten my Yarmouth present yet!' was the reply.

Peer loon! Some years later just shortly after his wedding, he was lost with all his shipmates when the *Quiet Waters* disappeared in a storm in 1954.

Aye! The Yarmouth Present was a highly prized gift but it was seldom expensive. How could it be? Apart from the immediate straitened financial situation, it had to be borne in mind that in a very few weeks 'Suntie Claas' would be expected to come doon the lum on Hogmanay Nicht (not Christmas Eve).

So thus the balance between 'fisher bairns' and 'toonser bairns' was redressed. While the fisher bairns were the envy of their classmates at Yarmouth time, 'Suntie' in due season was remarkably mean towards them! Ye canna get it twice!

But let's get back to Yarmouth River where the fleet was more or less ready to call at Seaham or Shields on the way home. There they would pick up several tons of coal, not for bunkers but 'for the hoose'.

The fish hold would be half filled with the best household coal at nineteen shillings a ton! Now, there was a 'richt Yarmouth present'! Less than a pound per ton. Shades of Scargill and MacGregor!

Each member of the crew could have a share of the coal

according to the capacity of his coal-sheddie. This was common practice for many years until there was some dibber-dabber aboot 'usin' fishin' boats for cargo boats' and finally the practice ceased. No doubt the local coal merchants had 'kickit up a stink'.

Well now, here was I on that Saturday night on the hunt for suitable presents. That didn't take me very long – gloves for the wife and a toy tea-set for the bairn, but my companion, a shipmate, seemed very difficult to please.

'Ye see, Peter,' says he 'My quine's gettin' her granny's organ fin she kicks the bucket an' seein' that the wifie's gey aul' noo it's time the quine wis learnin'! I'm lookin' for special music 'til 'er!'

I stood at the door of every music shop in Yarmouth in turn until I wis fair scunnert. On his exit, empty handed, from the umpteenth shop I demanded in exasperation.

'Fit is't ye're lookin' for onywye? Is't a Bach Fugue or a Mendelssohn Sonata? Ye're jist a fashious brute!'

'Oh no!' says he 'It's nae naethin' lik 'at! I'm lookin' for yon kin o' stuff that the darkies sings! Somethin' aboot a Sweet Chariot, ye ken!'

'That'll be Negro Spirituals that ye're needin' says I.

'O'gweed help's is 'at fit ye ca't? I've been seekin' spooky music!'

The great baa-heidit oof!

Crafty conquistador fae St Catharine's Dub

The Don was a tall strappin' chiel whose dark good looks might well have been envied by the stars of the silent films.

His swarthy handsomeness was accentuated by the white of his teeth when he smiled and by the tiny gold earrings which he wore, not for ornamentation, but in the sincere belief that earrings improved the eyesight.

This strange belief was common among seafarers of his generation, some of whom maintained stoutly that having the ears pierced was sufficient in itself, but I'm sure that this defence of half-measures was simply an attempt to conceal the fact that the price of the earrings was beyond them.

Some folk said there was gipsy blood in the Don. Others, less charitable, said it was 'tinkie bleed' for his Deydie (gran'dad) had been a roving tinker selling pots and pans and his granny had been a kitchie-deem at Balmoral.

Both rumours were utterly wrong, for the Don was, in all probability, a real Don, descendant of the sole survivor of the Spanish galleon which lies in St Catharine's Dub, near Collieston harbour. *Santa Catarina* was the galleon's name.

Balmoral? Never! A Spanish castle? Aye! Surely! I'm thinkin' that for many generations the Don's forebears had wrested a precarious living from the sea along the Buchan coast.

From tiny settlements like Collieston and the Old Castle at Slains, they had plied their trade in small boats, catching herring in season, but relying mainly on sma'-lines with mussel bait for haddock, whiting and codling, not forgetting the 'plashies' (plaice) which were plentiful along the shore.

Their source of bait, the Ythan estuary, could hardly have been handier.

Since there were no fishmarkets then, the fishers had to dispose of their own catches so we find the women-folk 'traivlin' far up-country with their creels of fish on their backs, bartering their fish for farm-produce, butter, cheese, eggs or an antrim hen.

Seldom indeed were there any cash deals, for the country folkies had nae siller. Still, the practice flourished for centuries, but it must have presented problems if a body wis needin' a pair o' boots or a sark!

Foo mony huddicks for a pair o' breeks? Foo muckle hard fish for a linner? (flannel shirt)

Speakin' aboot hard fish have ye ever tasted a speldin'? No? Then ye dinna ken fit ye're missin'!

Speldins were whitings split and cleaned then liberally salted prior to drying in the summer sun. These dried whitings were very tasty indeed and for many a long year Collieston speldins were renowned.

From far and near folk came to the village for the dazzling white fishies which were spread all over the place to dry.

I'm tellin' ye, the Ritz couldna offer ye onything to beat a speldin roassen (roasted) on a branner abeen an open fire. Serve with home-made 'breid' (oatcake) and country butter. Wow!

I ken for a fact that mony a youngster took the speldin by the tail and scoffed the lot, bone and all, leaving only the 'lug-been'.

Sadly, Collieston speldins are now only memories. You see, the men who caught the whitings and the wives who processed them have long since departed and have never been replaced.

Now then, the need for bigger boats and better harbours drove the Don's forebears to seek pastures new. A bourachie o' them settled in Boddam where they are reputed to have hang't the monkey.

Jist watch the Boddamers! Once in a generation or it micht be two – the interval grows wider as time goes by – you'll see a tall dark Adonis wi' flashin' een. He should really ha'e a pointed beard, a helmet, a horse, a lance an' a sword!

Ten to one his name is Stephen or Philip. Ye'll see the same thing aboot the Broch. Fancy? Well, if the Buchans came oot o' the Ark the chances are that the Stephens and Philips came oot o' a galleon. Maybe they are entitled to royalties on sherry!

But the Don that I kent was a Peterheid chiel, a fisherman and a good hand at that. Strictly inshore, of course! Not for him the wide open ocean wastes like the Viking or Bergen Banks.

He clung doggedly to the old methods, sma'-lines, cod nets (they are not a modern innovation) and the ripper. Then, with the advent of the motor engine, he branched into trawling for flukes (flat fish).

The Don was also a harbour pilot. For a few bob per annum, he obtained from the Harbour Trustees a licence which permitted him to display on the bows of his boatie a large 'P' (official pilot).

Since there were about a dozen such craft in the port, there was great rivalry between their skippers, for first aboard the steamer got the job of piloting her into port.

In those days Peterhead had a thriving trade in timber, salt and coal along with the export of vast quantities of cured herring in barrels.

Mostly illiterate, these pilots knew their own coast and its tides like the backs of their hands and they were first-rate men at their job.

Strange as it may seem, all rivalry disappeared when the sound of the 'Lifeboat guns' was heard, for these same lads were always the lifeboat crew. Then the only rivalry was to see who could be first aboard!

Now, I did mention trawling, and here lay the Don's great weakness, for he was an inveterate poacher! Fancy that now! Oh aye! He was convinced that a box of fish from forbidden waters had a value far in excess of anything caught legally. He was not, and never will be alone in that belief.

Came the day when he was 'catched' with his boat full o' fish and her propellor full of rope! Summoned to appear before the Sheriff in Aberdeen a week later, he spurned the local train and made the trip in his ain boatie.

Of course, he trawled all the way there, paid his substantial fine in court, then trawled all the way home, beating all the existing records for one day's fishing. A proper conquistador!

The Don's favourite stamping ground lay between Rattray Head and the Broch. From Rattray Head to the Cairnbulg Beacon you are in a bay called the Cample, and there the flukes are the world's best, as long as a fish-box and almost as broad, with spots as big as half-croons. Eight or maybe ten to the box!

It was risky to lift such a fish with one hand 'cos she could 'brak yer thoom' if she twisted her tail. How do I know? Let that flee stick to the wa'!

From the Beacon northwards you are in the Broch Bey and there the flukes are not quite so big. Ye'll get fifteen o' them into a box.

It was the Don's custom to nip into the Broch just before the chip shops closed then he sent one of his two crew members for a sixpenny supper, which would normally contain two fish, but since the shop was about to close he never failed to get an extra haddock and a double dose o' chips.

Enough to give the three musketeers a good meal. A fly bird, the crow! Then the night's trawling would be resumed.

'An' far wis the Brochers a' this time?' ye may say.

At Barra Heid or the Butt o' Lewis or shelterin' for their lives in some Hielan loch!

Now, to the hardy breed of men who sail the stormy seas with the letters FR on their boats, let me give this earnest warning.

Jist watch this move that's on the cards eynoo t' lat the Spaniards intil the Common Market, 'cos if they're onything like the Don they winna be contintit wi' yer fish.

They'll be needin' yer chips ana'!

To catch a herrin', first throw a concrete block

In the late 1940s, there was a sudden boom in the building of kippering kilns throughout the north-east. The long-suffering British public were now to be provided with the luscious kippers which had been denied them for several years.

However, when it came to the crunch, the public had got themselves acclimatised to spam and powdered egg so the demand for kippers was unexpectedly poor.

The kippering kilns were built with concrete blocks which had suddenly appeared on the scene as acceptable building material, but most people looked on the cement blockies as pure rubbish which 'wid faa doon an' kill aabody'!

Still, these same kilns are in use today as net factories, tyre depots etc, and they hinna faan doon yet!

At that time we were seine-netting in a 75 foot MFV which was a fine craft. She would be even better if we were to put in extra ballast to offset the weight of the great muckle deck-house, so with this in mind, we acquired a lorry load of the cement blockies and stowed them beneath the floor of the fishroom.

This greatly improved the boat's stability and we soon forgot they were there.

There was a persistent rumour for a while that a certain eminent building firm had gone bust 'cos somebody had stolen aa their blockies! Jist a rumour!

As one of our crew remarked to the baffled police searchers, 'Ye canna leave naething nooadays! They wid tak' the een oot o' yer heid an' come back for the holes!'

Winter wore into spring and soon it was time to switch to herring fishing. But altho' it was herrin' time, there was, alas, nae herrin', at least not on the local grounds.

Several skippers decided to try 'the boxin''. This meant going to far-away places such as the Patch or the Reef or even further. Any herrings caught would be iced into boxes and stowed below so that a second night's fishing could be carried out.

Of course, a bumper haul would mean an immediate return to port, but it was deemed prudent to be prepared for at least two nights at sea, for it was simply not possible to make the round trip in a day.

About half a score of boats, mostly steam drifters, left Peterhead at the back o' Sunday and steamed to the eastward until the evening, when it was time to shoot the nets.

Next morning proved that all had drawn a blank except our own good selves. We had fourteen crans which did not justify a return trip, so into the boxes they went, before being iced and covered with sheets of grease-proof paper.

Then they had to be stowed oot o' the road in the side-lockers or 'wings' of the hold. What a job!

You see, the wings of the hold, owing to the shape of the boat are very narrow at the bottom but wide at the top, so stowing these boxes was like building a pyramid upside down.

Eventually we got them secured, but not without a few jammed fingers and several bad words!

All that day we dodged further to the east, for apparently we had not got far enough the first night.

There was ample time in the afternoon to sleep or to read whatever was at hand.

That afternoon I had been reading an article in a very posh publication, concerning the remarkable prowess of certain ring-net fishermen in the Firth of Clyde.

According to the article, the herring was an unpredictable beastie which clung to the seabed all day and rose to the surface at night. I knew this to be true just as I knew that they didn't always rise far enough!

These fishermen had discovered a method of bringing the herring up to a point where their net could reach them! The secret was to have on deck a few bags of sand. The skipper, having located the herring shoal on the seabed, would order his crew to sprinkle handfuls of sand into the sea, while he steered the boat zig-zag across the shoal.

The sand would sink to the bottom, where it would kittle the herrin's backs and gar them rise!

'Well, well!' says I, 'I've heard a lot, but this beats aa!'

That night, when we had shot our nets, it was decided that the concrete blockies were now surplus to requirements and should therefore be dumped overboard.

During this, I expressed the humble opinion that 'if herrin' wid rise, ower the heids o' a suppie o' san', they wid ging berserk if we drappit cement blocks on their heids!' We would be fortunate indeed to see a net in the morning! We would 'loss the lot'!

Brother John merely shook his head and said:

'Niver mind 'im! he's only makkin that up!'

Well now, when we started to haul at 1 a.m., we could do nothing at all with the first net. She was absolutely ram-stam full o' herrin', and five crews couldn't have hauled her.

Before our eyes the net tore to ribbons with the strain, and we managed to save only a few fragments. This was disaster indeed, for we had eighty nets to haul.

The second net, however, was not nearly so heavily fished, having only some three crans in her, which was more than plenty. Thereafter the nets were in no danger and we finished up with 170 crans. Then it was full butt for Peterhead. One of my mates remarked: 'It's funny that the overloaded net was nearest to the spot where we dumped the blocks! It's a good job we didna steam, along the fleet o' nets drappin' blocks a' the wye!'

When I made no reply he asked: 'Did 'ee ken that the herrin' wid rise like yon?'

'Certainly!' said I. 'Didn't I warn ye aforehand?'

Neither to him, nor to anyone else, would I confess that I hadn't believed one word of the article.

The drawbacks of rubber boots!

For the magnificent weekly wage of thirty-four shillings and tenpence, Jeemsie was cook on the drifter *Meadowsweet*.

In today's decimal coinage his pay would be £1.74. For that amount of cash he had to cook every meal for ten men and keep the cabin and the galley clean.

He had to haul the nets like any deckie and assist in the discharging of the catch and, while he was not obliged to keep a watch at the wheel, he was duty bound to relieve the skipper at meal times.

He was not required to keep a watch at the nets and, should the shippie be away from home, as she often was for weeks at a time, he was not obliged to make the supper on Sunday. What a concession!

Peer Jeemsie, like the rest o's, didna ken ony better!

Behold now our hero in the shippie's cabin at 1 a.m., that witching hour when fishermen keep their tryst with the silver darlings. The crew have just had their 'tay' and Jeemsie is donning a brand new pair of rubber boots.

'Ye surely dinna ha'e big feet my loon!' says the Turk.

'No, skipper, they're nae big. Six an' a half.'

'Man!' says the Turk, 'fin I wis your age I had the bonniest feeties on the East coast. The quines fairly likit t' dunce wi' me, I wis sic a bonny duncer! The Hielan' deems jist gid wild fin I took them up for a wultz. I think it wis my little feeties that did it!'

'Fit's come ower yer feeties noo, skipper?' says Duncan the driver. 'Did ye meet in wi' a traction engine or something?'

The Turk ignored this sally and addressed Jeemsie thus: 'Ye shouldna wear rubber boots, my loon!'

'Foo nae, skipper?'

'Weel, my loon, there's an affa suction in them. They'll sook yer feet like twa poultices then ye'll ging blin'! Rubber boots is affa sair on young men's een!'

'Fa telt ye that, skipper?'

'Yon mannie that has the boot shop in the Longate.'

'Aye, aye,' says Jeemsie drily, 'he sells leather boots, I suppose'!

'Dam't,' says Duncan, 'I'll ha'e to write to my brither at Povertyknap (pronounce the K) an' tell 'im aboot this suction ferlie. His wife's an eeseless bizzom an' she maks a poor shape at milkin' the coo.

'If she sticks a pair o' rubber boots on the coo's udder she winna need to touch the beast ava! She winna even need a pail – the boots'll kep the milk!'

'Aafa clivver!' laughed the Turk, 'but ye canna beat the leather'!

'Weel,' says Jeemsie, 'fit wye div ye ha'e t' thump an' stump like an elephant t' get yours on, an' gettin' them aff's jist like a horse gettin' shaved?'

'Niver mind that! Ho-ro lads, let's get a start!' says the skipper. Then a second later as he heaved his bulk up the trap, 'Good grief, I've torn my breeks on a nail! But that'll ha'e t' wyte.'

The crew trooped forrard to where the deck was brightly lit by the two acetylene lamps on the wheelhouse front. The after half of the vessel remained in darkness.

With a hiss of steam the captain took the strain on the heavy rope which was pulled into the rope-locker and coiled neatly there by the fireman.

Slowly but surely the vessel moved ahead and soon the first net was being dragged aboard like a great sheet.

The silvery shimmer of herring brought a ripple of excitement expressed in the tender words of endearment uttered by each and every man. 'Swim up you little dears! Come away now stick your little heads in! Let this day be spoken about! Just a few more please!'

Duncan never ceased to wonder why his shipmates should unfailingly resort to English when they implored the herring to come to them. They would coax and cajole and wheedle as if the herring were a reluctant maid. Oh, the feel fishers!

When the net had been hauled, it was immediately slacked away again. 'We'll gi'e her half-an-hour yet' says the Turk.

This was common practice. It was simply an effective way of finding out whether the fish were still swimming. The first go at the nets was always called 'Lookin' on'.

'Half a cran in her: that's a good markin'!' says the

skipper. 'Jeemsie, my loon, I wid shue this hole in my breeks but it wid mean takin' my boots aff an' ye ken fit that is!'

'Fine div I ken that,' was the reply. 'But we'll try't athoot the boots an' breeks comin' aff.

So down to the engine room went the Turk for repairs. Duncan had difficulty threading the needle so he passed it to Jeemsie whose deft fingers made a very neat job of stitching on the stooping Turk's starboard hip.

'Dinna ging ower deep wi' the needle' says Duncan. 'It widna dee t' job the mannie! Gweed folk's scarce ye ken!'

The repair completed it was time to haul in earnest. Almost a basket of herring had meshed in the clean net so, at the skipper's 'Haul awa', lads' the crew buckled to with a will.

It was warm, hard work, teamwork par excellence, a skill gained from long years at the job with never a man putting a finger through a mesh. Only greenhorns did that!

Duncan the chief, was on the side-deck beside the wheel-house working a scum-net which was really a gigantic butterfly net with a heavy pole.

With this he was retrieving some of the herring which had fallen loose from the nets; these were usually the cream of the crop and were the perks for the chief, the fireman and the cook. 'Scum,' they were called (the herrin', I mean).

The nets were about 'half hauled' when the skipper, who was at the cork-raip summoned Duncan, 'Tak' a hud o' this raip a meenit Duncan. I'll ha'e t' run!' And with that he disappeared into the shadows near the stern.

'Ho-ho!' chuckled Jeemsie, 'So the skipper wants to be alone. Well, it's his ain blame – he winna bide awa' fae pey soup.'

His laughter was cut short by an unearthly yell from the darkness 'Come wi' a knife Duncan! Hing in man, hing in! Come wi' a knife!'

Duncan ran immediately but he was back in less than a minute, folding his pocket knife before slipping it into his pocket. With a warning shake of the head he gazed at Jeemsie.

'Jeemsie, my freen, ye'll hear the riot act read the day! Ye'll get "Who broke the hurley!" I tellt ye nae t' ging ower deep wi' the needle but ye didna listen. Ye great goat, ye shewed the mannies' breeks 'til 'is sark so he couldna get a start. I wis jist in time!'

The returning skipper said nothing but the glower he gave the cook spoke volumes.

About six o'clock in the morning the shippie was under way with the delighted skipper in a forgiving mood. Well, he had a bonny shot, hadn't he? Eighty or ninety cran was a great night's work.

In fear and trembling the cook came to take the wheel so that the Turk could go aft for his tay. But the expected storm did not materialise. Instead, the skipper gave the youngster a playful punch on the shoulder.

'I believe ye did yon deliberate, ye coorse skate! Ye're an affa lad!'

'Na, na, skip, nae me!' says Jeemsie. 'I wisna seein' richt fin I wis using the needle. Maybe it wis the rubber boots sookin' my feet!'

The ghost in the white seemit

Skipper Bob McTurk (The Turk) had suffered a major defeat at the hands of his better half.

For years she had begged him to change into lighter clothing when the bonny days came round but her pleas had fallen on deaf ears.

Now, her patience finally exhausted, she sailed in with all guns blazing.

'Ye great greasy clort that ye are! Ilkie time I wash yer shift the claes-tow braks wi' the wecht.

'You should ging up to Jimmy Reid's an' get a horse, then get a soord an' a battle axe fae the museum.

'I'll gi'e ye my ain coal-pail for a helmet but ye winna need armour! Nae wi' a shift like that!

'Then ye can flee the hills like Sir Lancelot!'

Under such an onslaught the poor Turk wilted. But on one point he was adamant; he would on no account wear shorts.

'They micht dee for liftin' a het kettle but they wid nivver hap me!'

Neither would he visit a shop. So, in view of his enormous girth, nothing would suffice but to get 'a sicht o' drawers an' semmits fae the shop' so that he could 'wale' among them at his leisure.

But still there was one great problem. Any drawers that fitted his middle would need a fathom cut from the legs; if they fitted his legs they would need a yard of elastic at the top!

No semmit would fit him athoot a great muckle gushet shued into the front.

What a maneer! Claes a' ower the place like a stallie on the Broadgate!

It took a long time to reach a happy compromise but at last the mannie was riggit oot and the unwanted garments were baled in readiness for their return to the shop.

On the Monday morning our gallant hero left the house to go to the harbour.

Oh boys this was fine! Pure fresh air was circulating where fresh air had seldom been before.

This was life, this was freedom as if a door had been opened!

Then in one blinding second panic filled his breast.

There couldn't possibly be such a free flow of air unless there was a doorie open!

Good grief! Had he forgotten to fasten certain vital buttons?

A quick downward glance would reassure him, but his washin'-hoose biler o' a belly decreed that this was impossible.

He could hardly ficher wi' buttons in the street so he would turn back.

Turn back on a Monday? Never! All the bad luck in Scotland would be his if he did that!

He could stop a passing boy with a question 'Hey my loon! Is my shoppie door open?' but he didna like!

Were he to venture up a close for a quick check some wifie would be sure to doubt his intentions and would chase him wi' a broom bidding him 'Ging an' dee that at yer ain gate en'!'

The situation was critical but not entirely out of hand.

The Turk's mither wit led him to the nearest shop window where his own reflection assured him that all was well.

So the gentle breezes were part and parcel of his new found freedom? Great!

Thus in a happier mood he reached the pier where his own darling *Meadowsweet* awaited him.

Oh, what a steer! Horses an' cairts by the score.

At least a hunner crews busy at their nets.

Coal-heavers walking the precarious planks with ten stone bags of coal on their backs just like black ballet dancers on a heaving stage, dropping their load with unerring aim into the pit of the drifter's bunker.

Message boys with their baskets and watermen with their hoses; it was all go, for the armada was preparing to sail in the afternoon.

What a bonny day it was! Half the toon was on the pier to see the shippies gaun oot.

Since it was Monday, the guttin' quines half day, scores of them were down to wave cheerio to their lads and husbands.

Even Mrs McTurk was there wi' twa bairns at her tail an' twa in the coach (pram).

As the *Meadowsweet* rounded the jetty the Turk stuck his arm out of the wheelhouse window to wave to his excited offspring and in so doing he got a welcome blast of fresh air aneth his oxter.

Late that evening the *Meadowsweet* lay at her nets some forty miles east-by-north off Peterhead.

She lay head to wind at the leeward end of a mile of nets which hung like a great curtain two fathoms below the surface.

The shippie was tethered by a thick tarry rope which ran the whole length of the nets and on this rope she would be heaved ahead in the morning when the process of hauling would begin.

It was a lovely evening with the sun sinking behind a low bank of dark cloud, a sure sign of westerly wind to come.

Close astern a great white carpet of birds had settled on the calm waters to await their breakfast from the nets. Now and then the silence was gently broken by the soft 'Whoo-oof' of a herring whale.

Monday night meant that there was no back-log of sleep to catch up on so the crew were rather slower than usual to turn in.

They sat for a while behind the wheelhouse discussing the past weekend and vieing with each other in identifying the vessels nearest to them.

As far as the eye could see there were ships on the same errand as themselves. Each one had her mizzen sail set and her two paraffin riding lights becoming more readily visible in the gathering dark.

Then, as if by common consent, all hands went below to turn in, leaving one man to keep watch.

There would be three one-hour watches and the last man would 'mak e' tay' at 1 a.m.

In the cabin there was a shocked silence as the skipper removed his breeks before turning in.

'This is something new, boys! Here's a man gaun in ower athoot 'is breeks!

'The days o' miracles is surely nae past efter aa! An' fit's this he's wearin'?

'Surely nae fite drawers an' a fite seemit? Ye never saw the like afore, did ye?

'Nivver! It's a mercy we're a' spared!'

Of course Jeemsie the cook started to snicker and when he whispered 'Moby Dick, the great white whale!' the dam burst and the crew laughed themselves silly.

Folk'll nivver believe this! But the amusement faded rapidly when the Turk disappeared into his bunk, treating his men with silent contempt.

The man on watch in the wheelhouse knew nothing of this.

Nor was he aware that about eleven o'clock the Turk had come on deck in his new outfit to have a look at the nicht and to listen intently for the quiet 'plop' of herrin' loupin'.

The watchman came aft at his appointed time to call his relief. Then suddenly his hair stood on end for there on the starboard quarter stood a ghostly figure, 'clothed in white samite, mystic, wonderful'.

The poor deckie gave one piercing yell of terror and bolted!

'Od, there maun be something wrang wi' that loon!' says the Turk and he ambled forrard in the wake of the terror stricken youth whose yell had brought three of his mates on deck in a state of alarm.

But when these fellas got on deck, the sound of running feet was away in the fore part of the vessel so they set off to investigate.

At the end of the first lap the thunder of feet brought the rest of the crew on deck in a hurry and they too joined in the hunt.

Towards the end of the fourth lap the Turk tripped on a pond board and fell clyte on his belly.

His crew promptly fell on top of him and there was a great stramash.

The sole survivor had scooted down to the cabin and into his bunk like a frightened rabbit.

It was a gey sheepish and tired crew who silently took their tay at 1 a.m. The skipper for all his bulk was the fittest of the lot.

'Now, lads,' says he, 'If ye're gaun t' run a marathon ye're better t' wear the richt gear for 't. Y'll nivver see the winnin' post wi' hairback breeks an' worsit drawers on!'

'That's fit I had on,' says the watchman, 'an' I bate the 'hale lot o' ye!'

19

Leebie's solid sheelters

The eastern sky was pink with the first hazy rays of the rising sun when Leebie, sick again, rose from her bed. As she knelt on the floor and retched miserably into a pail – there was no sink – she reflected rather bitterly, 'This'll be the fifth een an' the aul'est een's nae at the school yet! It's jist nae richt o' oor John Willie t' dee this t' me!'

John Willie, the man of the house, had left for the sea some two hours earlier with his beautiful baited haddock line in a huge wicker scull balanced on his hip. Not till dinner time would he return with his appetite whetted by the sea and several hours' work. Fish or no fish, he would be hungry!

Od, he wis aye hungry, the bairns were aye hungry and it was cook and scrub and wash and bait fae brak' o' sky till lang efter dark! There wis aye a something!

Leebie pulled herself thegither then dichtit her face wi' the flannel clootie afore she lookit oot at the door towards the foreshore less than fifty yards distant. The tide was perfect for gaitherin' mussels.

It was time she was at the scaap – she could see some women there already – so drawing a thick tartan shawl round her shoulders she hastened to the shore, mussel basket in hand. In the basket there was a crude iron tool which John Willie had fashioned for her to tear the mussels from the rocks.

Long experience had taught Leebie that to gather bait with bare hands was to invite lacerated fingers. Slacken the mussels first, then gather them into the basket.

A few months earlier a 'hale cairt-load o' mussels had arrived in the village from the Ythan estuary. The load had been shared out by guesswork among the different families and each family carried its own 'heap' to the rocky shore where the mussels were spread in a position where the tide could reach them daily, thus keeping them alive.

Each family mussel-patch was called 'the scaap' and was separated from its neighbours by little dykies o' steens. The mussels soon clung to the rocks and could be obtained by the women (always the women) when the tide permitted. Honesty was seldom questioned but when

Job wrote yon versie, 'Some remove the landmarks', I'm sure he was writin' aboot the mussel scaaps.

Leebie kent her bairns would sleep a lang time yet so she took the opportunity for a news with her neighbours while they gathered their bait. Janet, one of the senior members of the group raised a bit of a laugh when she remarked, on seeing Leebie's pale face, 'Aye, Aye my quine, ye're just like the lave o' hiz fishermen's wives! Ye're expected t' be a horse a' day an' a meer aa nicht!' Nobody contradicted her but there were a few blushes on the cheeks of the younger women.

Her basket filled, Leebie carried it to the house where she had a quick peep at her sleeping bairns before returning to the scaap for more mussels. Then it was time to start on the daily household chores, for her brood would soon be clamouring for their porridge.

Altho' every drop of water had to be carried fae the waal in the street, and altho' there was no sanitation, Leebie's hoosie was spotless, as were also her bairns. Certainly there were fool faces and hands at times but ye ken bairns that are fool temporarily fae bairns that are forever yirdit!

The hoosie, like so many others, comprised a butt and a ben wi' a little closetie in the middle, and had been hame to several generations of John Willie's folk.

The said John Willie duly arrived for his denner with his line in its scull, but now the line required to be 'redd'. This would be his work in the afternoon, unravelling the long line and replacing any missing hooks (wants). When he had finished, the line would be ready for baiting again.

While he was engrossed in this task Leebie would sheel (shell) the mussels using a futtle (gutting knife) to slit the shells open and with a deft flick of the wrist to skite the juicy mussel into a clean pail. This was an art, a skill gained over years of practice. Meanwhile, the aul'est quine would rock her little sister in the cradle while the twa loons played aboot the door.

The bairns soon learned to keep clear of the line with its barbed hooks. A skelp or twa fairly helped their learning.

When the mussels had been sheeled Leebie took the empty 'shaals' and dumped them on the shore. The pail of juicy bait was laid aside until later; she would bait the line when the bairns were beddit, for then she would get peace and quiet.

The baiting would take her about two hours and she would need all the mussels in the clean pail to bait the 450 hooks. John Willie would have the line all ready for her, neatly coiled in a basket with every hook 'stuck', i.e. the horse-hair tippin was twined lightly round the hook so that when Leebie drew the line through her hand the points of the hooks were pointed away from her. Thus the hooks didn't get entangled in the line itself, and it also saved the baiter's fingers.

Leebie would coil the line neatly into the great wicker scull, baiting each hook skilfully, laying the baited hooks in rows across the mouth of the scull and separating the rows with layers of fresh grass. Everything had to be done with meticulous care so that the line would run clear in the dark o' the mornin'.

Aye! Leebie had few spare meenits aa her mairried life! She bore her trials and tribulations with a cheerful heart but one thing really got her riled, and this was the theft of her sheeled mussels by the loons of the village. These rascals could have got plenty of mussels on the shore to bait the bits o' line that they amused themselves with, but why ficher wi' mussels in their shells when they could pinch a few from Leebie's pail?

You see Leebie had the habit of putting her pail of sheeled mussels outside the door in the evening, to prevent the pail being 'cowpit' in the steer as she washed and beddit the bairns. The loons kent far Leebie's pail wis left an' they kent that if they were stealthy and swift at the same time they could get 'solid sheelters' (plenty of shelled mussels).

It grieved Leebie that the fruits of her labours were being pilfered, leaving her occasionally short of bait for her own line.

In vain she cyardit the loons – they just leuch and ran.

'Ee'll sup sorra wi' the speen o' grief, gin I catch ye!' she would yell at them, to no avail, for fine did they ken that wi' their fleetness they were safe.

But this particular night there came to Leebie a brilliant idea whose simplicity and certain dire effect made her chuckle in anticipation.

Among all the pails that Leebie required, one of the most important was the 'orra pail', the slop-bucket which was teemed at least twice daily where the cleansing tide would remove all traces. Now, with fower bairns in a hoosie that lacked sanitation that bucket could fyles contain some gey ferlies!

So, in the gathering dark Leebie substituted the orra pail for the mussel pail and waited inside the door for results. Soon she heard the stealthy approach, the short pause as two cupped hands scooped their loot from the brimming bucket, then the head-long flight of the juvenile marauder.

In a few seconds she heard his jubilant cry to his pals, 'Solid sheelters boys! Solid sheelters!' then, 'Oh gyaad! oh gyaad!'

Then Leebie doubled up with laughter, kennin' that never again would the rascals raid her mussel pail. But as she enjoyed her unaccustomed mirth a sudden stab of pain brought her up sharp and she muttered to herself, 'Oh Lord, it's jist nae richt o' oor John Willie t' dee this t' me!'

There's aye a something, Leebie!

An underwater treasure trove

I am convinced that, at some time in his career, every fishing skipper has had a wonderful dream in which he discovers an underwater hidden valley whose bottom is as smooth as a bowling green.

Of course this hidden valley is surrounded by peaks and ridges of jagged rock where no net could possibly survive but which by the same token form a perfect refuge for millions of fish of every kind.

The floor of the valley is literally spear-deep with prime flatfish; lemon soles and plaice will scarcely be able to find a parking space between the tiers of giant halibut, and immediately above this priceless treasure cod and haddock of divine proportions gambol to and fro like great flocks of sheep.

Only at great cost has this skipper managed to locate the valley, as masses of torn netting and broken ropes festooning the surrounding precipices will testify, but now that he has the key to this priceless treasure, he keeps the dark secret to himself.

Only when there are no other vessels in sight will he venture to drag his net across the valley floor and only when the diamond market is sky-high will he dip into this boundless treasure store.

Ah well! There's nothing to stop a fella from dreaming, I suppose. But such places, if they ever existed, have long since been accurately charted and relentlessly fished bare, for modern fishing gear and high powered diesels allied to unbelievable electronics have alas left no refuge whatsoever for the denizens of the deep.

Conservation means a lot in the dictionary but it doesn't mean a thing on the sea where every skipper except oneself is just a blasted pirate!

There is however, an alternative dream to the aforementioned idyll and that is to find a wreck which nobody else knows about! Preferably this wreck should be a ship which died peacefully and not as the result of some cataclysmic explosion which has scattered great masses of debris over a wide area.

No, she is much better if she is a 'clean' wreck for then you can get your net close to the sunken ship which, as a rule, has a great attraction for fish. Such wrecks do exist!

I well remember going from Peterhead to Sheerness in a drifter early in 1940. We called at Hartlepool for coal and from there southward it was impossible to steer a straight course because of the masts and funnels of mined ships which littered the fairway.

There must have been many more which had disappeared completely. The seabed for many miles in all directions from the Tyne entrance is strewn thickly with wrecks.

In the 1950s with the advent of the Decca Navigator it was possible to pinpoint these wrecks and plot them on an accurate chart so that one could fish between them. At first this was highly profitable but, since there was no rich area of jagged peaks nearby to replenish the valley floor, the fish were gradually fished up, especially when more skippers got to know the exact location of every ship. So it was a case of 'Find your own wreck'!

This we managed to do, quite by accident. Away on our own, seeking pastures new, we unwittingly encircled a bobby-dazzler of a ship in our seine net gear and were promptly brought to a sudden halt. But with great patience and not a little skill gained in the hard school of experience we managed to retrieve our gear without serious loss.

Then we steamed slowly to and fro above the sunken Goliath, marking her outline on the echo sounder and plotting her exact length and beam on our home-made chart. For quite a while we managed to keep her location secret, and we did very well off that ship.

Although the fish were seldom plentiful around her, the quality was always supreme. But, like most secrets, her location finally leaked out and she became known as she still is known as Peter's Wreck. I suppose few if any of those skippers who fish around her now know who Peter was. I'm sure they don't care!

One lovely November day we were fishing in that area, some eighteen miles east-south-east of the Tyne, when a cargo vessel stopped beside us, waiting for our net to break surface. Flying the Dutch flag she was from Montrose for the Mediterranean with a cargo of seed tatties which would probably come back to Montrose in the summer as choice Cyprus spuds.

When we hauled the net we went right alongside with the fry her skipper had requested. 'Two baskets of haddocks please!' On seeing my surprised glance he explained that he had on board a big chest freezer which was crying out for fresh fish, so two baskets it was. And the price? Two cartons of Lucky Strike fags and the biggest bottle of booze I have ever seen, freely offered and willingly accepted. The plunder was placed in my bunk while we carried on fishing.

Late that night, in Shields Gut, the great share-out took place. It was Saturday night and, since we did not fish on Sundays, there was no hurry to turn in, so we sat for a while reading our mail over a leisurely joog o' tay.

'I've been thinkin' aboot the swag, says the cook.

'There's five o's athegither; we a' smoke but only twa o's taks a drink, gie hiz twa the bottle an' pairt the fags amon' the three o' ye.'

Everybody agreed so the two rascals mittened the bottle, a great muckle square thing that held about half a gallon. The print on the label was foreign and the contents were crystal clear. The delighted pair put a drappie in their tay and judging by the smack of their lips and the sparkle in their eyes, it was first class. And so to bed.

I was rudely awakened at 1 a.m. by the sound of our two heroes practically fighting each other for the toilet. 'Hing in, min! Come oot o' that an' lat me in!'

All day on Sunday it continued thus. In fact the two of them never donned their trousers at all.

'Coorse stuff yon!' says the cook. 'It comes through ye like bilin' leed!'

'Bilin' leed?' exclaimed his pal, 'Pirn threed's mair like it'!

But I was blinded by the sun!

In the modern fishing boat practically everything is controlled from the wheelhouse. It would be no problem for an experienced man to take a boat to sea by himself provided he knows how to start the engine.

But in the steam drifters this was not the case. The drifters' wheelhouse equipment comprised a steering wheel, a telegraph and a voice-pipe to the engine room, and an overhead compass. There had to be somebody in the engineroom to work the engine controls and fire the boiler.

These duties were carried out by the 'black squad', the chief and the fireman who, along with the cook received a weekly wage.

The chief's wages were 45 shillings, the fireman and the cook got 35 shillings per week, but they got no share of the catch. From their wages the chief, fireman and cook had to leave ten shillings weekly to pay for their food.

During the hauling of the nets the cook had to haul with the deckies, the fireman had to coil the tarry messenger rope and the chief had to be handy in case a few turns of the propellor were required from time to time. Since this was not often the case, the chief was free to wield a great muckle thing like a butterfly net on the end of a stout pole to retrieve any herrings which had fallen back into the sea from the nets.

This instrument was called a 'scummer' and on a good night the chief could catch a basket, maybe even two baskets of 'scum'. The proceeds from the sale of such herrings he shared with the fireman. If at the end of a week they had ten shillings apiece for 'scum' they would have thought they were doing well.

Many of the chiefs or 'drivers', as they were called, 'drove' the same shippies for several years, so much so that they became synonymous with the ships they sailed in. A good driver was a treasure – he was efficient and economical. He could save a bob or two here and there and in those days a bob or two counted for a great deal.

Such a man was Joe Tait. To me he was an aul' aul' mannie, who had been a drifter driver for many years. Since I was only 18 or so, I thought that Joe must be positively 'hairy moulded' with age though he was still going to sea. When the time came for Joe to quit 'the sea' he got himself a ripper boatie which was a great deal older than he was himself!

She was clinker-built (planks overlapping) and she rejoiced in the name *Star of Fame*. Her length? Say 18 feet. Sail or oars but no engine of any kind. So now that you have been introduced to Joe and his boat, I'll get on with my tale.

'Twas the month of December, 1935. I had just finished decarbonising the engine of our family boat which at that time was a 40 footer with a 36 h.p. Kelvin paraffin engine. In fact I had the engine running and was about to take the boat into the bay for a trial run, when down came a regular crewman asking: 'Fit aboot a go at the ripper? I hear the cod's jist solid at Boddam Heid!'

'I'm willin',' says I, 'But we've nae rippers'.

'Och! that's nae bother,' was the reply, 'I'll pinch my father's gear!' And that's exactly what he did, so, fully equipped we set out for the ripper grounds just north of Buchan Ness. We would fill the boat with prime cod. So we thought.

It was a lovely winter morning with the sun like a ball of golden fire. The glare reflected from the sea was positively blinding and since we were steering into the sun the effect was doubled. I have experienced the same dazzle while driving a car on a wet road on a winter morning. As soon as you drive into the sun you are blinded.

And so it happened that in the glittering brilliance we failed to see the *Star of Fame* dead ahead of us. At the very last moment I spotted the boatie and spun the wheel hard to starboard but alas it was too late. Our stern struck the boatie about two feet from her stern post, thus swinging her hard against our port side, as we steamed past. Joe's shipmate, Alex Findlay, managed to get one arm and one leg across our bulwark and held on like grim death until we came to his assistance.

Poor old Joe was not so agile and he was left standing in his rapidly-sinking boat. With the helm hard to starboard our vessel executed a tight circle and within a few seconds

I had her back alongside the casualty from whence we dragged the old man by the scruff of his neck backwards on to our deck.

By that time he was thigh-deep in water and apparently unable to move. His boatie sank immediately we had a grip of him. We salvaged the mast and the oars but the *Star of Fame* had been extinguished forever.

Of course I had to go and face the music at home. I need not trouble you with the details of that distressing episode except that it was made perfectly clear to me that had either Joe or his pal been lost we would have been in deep trouble, since we had no insurance cover whatsoever! Meanwhile, I would have to see about replacing the lost boat.

In the afternoon I went in fear and trembling to the Custom House which at that time was in the building now occupied by the British Legion. There I made a full report to the Registrar of Shipping (Mr Cardno), who searched his records diligently but without success for any trace of the *Star of Fame*. He must have seen that I was quite distressed for he tried his best to reassure me.

'Look here!' says he. 'That boat is not in my books so she must be about 100 years old! Since nobody has been drowned and there have been no injuries there will be no need for any court proceedings. Settle the affair between yourselves but watch that Joe doesn't demand a ransom for his boatie!'

At an informal afternoon meeting in Irvin's office Aul' Joe was quite adamant that for the loss of his boat and gear he 'wis needin' sax powen'! There was no dibber-dabber, sax powen it was and the salesman paid Joe on the spot. Salesmen can be very useful at times. Of course, he would have to be repaid later. At that time I didn't have sax shillin's.

A few weeks later I met Joe at the Cross Keys corner. Rather hesitantly I asked him 'Fit like, Joe?'

'My loon!' says he, 'Ye did me a richt gweed turn yon day! I took the bus to Port Errol an' there I bocht a boatie fae yon nae-weel mannie. I got a larry fae Jimmy Sutherland to tak' her to Peterheid an' Reuben's putten an engine oot o' a Baby Austin intil her. She gings like an evil speerit an' I nivver need to touch an oar noo! The best that ivver cam' doon!'

'My govies,' says I, 'That must ha'e cost ye a fortun' afore ye got her to sea!'

'It did that,' says Joe, 'About sax powen!'

He was simply delighted with his 'new' craft. Her present-day equivalent? Say £850!

The puff adder and the eskimo

If ye're lookin' for a worthy exponent of the Noble Art of Girnin' ye could try a Buchan fairmer that has blight amon' his tatties an' canker amon' his neeps.

On the ither han', ye could try a Gaimrick that's lost a nicht's fishin' at the 'heerin' ' (nae 'herrin' ').

The twa o' them wid mak' a pair!

But if it's superlative performance ye're efter, ye should ha'e a news wi' a native dyed-in-the-wool Boddamer. I'll guarantee that in less than five meenits ye'll ha'e a lump in yer throat an' the tears 'll be trippin' ye!

Even tho' the chiel's into his second million, ye'll come awa' wi' the impression that 'The Lord's better t' strangers than He is til's ain'! It's a gift, man, a gift!

In the Loquacity League, only goal-difference separates the Buckie Blaaver fae the Brocher that's hame fae Yarmouth wi' a gweed fishin', while in the Friendly Furlongs, the Lossie man runs neck an' neck wi' the Differ eence they've been half an hour in The Gallon Can.

Now, if by ony extraor'inar' chance ye're seekin' sheer brazen impidence, dinna ging by the Blue Toon! 'Twid be a waste o' time!

Here in my native town, the gifts of Effrontery and Mendacity have been so liberally bestowed that no other Scot can possibly 'hud a cannle' to the Bluemogganers.

Div ye want proof?

Well now, some fifty-odd years ago, a gang o' hiz loons wis playin' on the spendin' beach that faces ye as ye come into Peterheid Fishery Harbour. This beach is actually on the Queenie.

In those days, Peterhead had two entrances and it was not unusual for great shoals of mackerel to enter the port via the North Harbour and make their exit via the South Harbour.

Strange as it may seem, nobody wanted mackerel then, apart from the gulls and the delighted seals who gorged themselves on the silver bounty. The fish were at times literally in millions!

So it came to pass that on the afore-mentioned beach we managed to separate a baby seal fae its mither. We didna want to bad-use the beastie; we jist wanted a bittie

o' fun oxterin' an' clappin' the craitur chance aboot. Och, the beast wis apparently ha'ein' a lot o' fun tee, fin fa comes on the scene but a chiel ca'd English Harry.

Our intention of returning the pup to its mither was dashed when Harry confiscated our prize and made off with it. Half an hour later we saw him in earnest consultation with his pal 'Duff', a local whose nickname had been gained in a most unusual fashion.

Apparently 'Duff' had been on a battleship during the Great War and like so many fisher lads he was in constant hot water for not saluting his superiors.

One Christmas Day he was detailed to fetch from the main galley the duff for his mess, and while he was carrying the steaming monster on a great muckle tray he met Admiral Jellicoe to whom he made the earnest request: 'Will ye hud this duff till I salute ye?'

In shocked amazement the admiral took the proffered tray while Duff gave him a really smart salute before resuming his way with his precious load.

Well now, the day after Harry took the seal, a strange apparition was seen at Aikey Fair.

In a little broon 'tintie' made oot o' a drifter's hatch cover, there was a drifter's barkin'-tank.

The tank was about five feet long, three feet wide and four feet deep. Most drifters had such a tank for barking the herring nets.

This process entailed the periodic dipping of the nets in a boiling solution of cutch or bark which came from a Burmese tree and was reckoned to be a good preservative.

A steam hose from the drifter's boiler kept the water piping hot.

Barking the nets was a hot, laborious task which the fishermen didn't like, but without bark, cotton nets soon rotted.

So here was the tintie and here was the tank, filled to the brim with Ugie water, and in the water was our baby seal which had overnight become 'The strange monster from the Arctic'.

Beside the tank on one of Irvin's fish-boxes sat Chief

Yokiedoke from Greenland, clad in an astrakhan coat and a fur hat that had both seen better days.

On his lower legs he wore a pair of Russian boots that his wife 'couldna pit on 'cos her legs wis ower fat'.

This was the world's leading authority on Arctic wild-life and he bore an uncanny likeness to Duff fae Peter-heid. He spoke no English, apparently.

At the door of the tent stood the cashier-cum inter-preter, who was to translate into English any answers that Yokiedoke might give to certain questions.

Admission cost three maiks, bairns one maik, and the hardy sons of rustic toil who had parked their Raleigh bikes in the park across the road rolled up in goodly numbers.

The seal soon realised she was the centre of attraction and played a real star role, sending great skirps o' watter in all directions, much to the relief of Yokiedoke who was 'swytin' far the sheepie swytes'! It was the month of July, ye ken!

The favourite question, 'Fit dis she get for her brakfist?' was relayed to Yokiedoke whose standard reply was 'Easka mala doosh'!

This, being interpreted by Harry, meant 'She fairly likes a kipper'.

'Wid she ait neeps?' brought a series of queer grunts fae the Eskimo, meaning that there were no neeps inside the Arctic Circle.

The audience were suitably impressed and the siller wis comin' in like sklate steens until, about five o'clock, disas-ter in the shape o' a clivver loon fae Byth threatened the entire project.

'Hey, mannie!' says Byth to Harry. ''At's nae a monster ata'! It's jist a common ilka-day seal! I'm seekin' ma maik back!'

In consternation, Harry glanced at Yokiedoke, won-dering what kind of grunt he would have to translate to pacify the now restive onlookers. Lesser mortals might have given up in despair, but the Bluemogganer streak in Yokiedoke rose nobly to his aid.

Rising majestically to his feet, like Davy Crockett, he addressed the loon, not in Eskimo but in the loon's ain tongue.

'She's nae a common ilka-day seal ata'! Onybody wi' a cork e'e could see that! She's a guaranteed genuine real-life Arctic Puff Adder, nivyer seen afore sooth o' the Great Ice Barrier Reef!'

Byth proved to be a thrawn kin' o' chiel.

'An' fit mak's a common seal a puff adder?' says he.

''Cos she farts in the tunk an' coonts the bubbles! That's fit mak's her a puff adder!' was the reply. 'An' onywye the shop's shut noo!'

There's the Bluemogganer for ye!

The pair o' rascals grabbed the seal, the tin wi' the maiks an' bolted, leaving the tent and the tank astarn.

Gross takings – three powen half-a-croon. Gross out-lay, nil. They nivver peyed for naething!

On the Monday, we got our seal back and promptly restored it to its mither that had been patrolling the har-bour entrance for twa 'hale days. Great was the joy in that reunion.

Later, when I described to Duff-Yokiedoke the expres-sion on the mither's face, I said it was 'Rapturous! Beatific!'

'There's a better word for that, my loon,' says he.

'It's "Easka mala doosh".'

An' he clinkit the maiks in 'is pooch.

When four walls equalled paradise

The floor of the room was 13 feet square. Since it was an upstairs room the side walls were perpendicular for about 4 feet and thereafter they followed the line of the roof-rafters so that the ceiling measured 13 feet × 4 feet.

The door was of tongue-and-groove boards on three cross-bars and it was so close to the side wall that the top right-hand corner had been cut off to follow the slope of the roof.

In local parlance this was 'a room wi' slopit wa's'! The door which opened on to a narrow landing had an old fashioned 'sneck' (latch).

The staircase from the landing to the ground floor had a twist of 135 degrees, so at one side the treads were very broad while at the other side they were almost non-existent. In the dark the stairs were a veritable death trap.

In the end wall of the room, directly opposite the door there was a recess about 1 foot deep and 6 foot high. This recess which served as a press (cupboard) had a few shelves but no door, and on its floor there was a gas meter which took pennies in its slot.

In the centre of the same wall there was an ancient, coal-burning black grate surrounded by a wooden 'Chumla' (mantelpiece). The grate had 'twa binks' (hobs) and an oven, and on the hearth there was a gas ring.

Near the right-hand end of the mantel shelf a gas bracket with its fragile mantle adorned the wall. This was for lighting the place.

From the single window nothing was visible but the slates of the house opposite, and a narrow strip of sky.

Close to the walls the floorboards were as new but most of the floor area was distinctly uneven as a result of the constant punishment it had received from a few generations of feet on its bare surface.

Only the knots in the boards retained anything like their original level. On the walls, the single thickness of paper had been varnished in the good old fisher style and the ceiling had at least a quarter inch of whitewash. The room was perfectly dry.

The nearest water tap was 'in the washin' hoose at the back o' the hoose' and this would mean a trip downstairs, along the front of the house and round to the back. The toilet was close to the washin' hoose, in the back-close.

Now it came to pass in the late thirties that James Forman Buchan (Jeemsie) and Elizabeth Reekie Buchan (Lisbeth) decided they would get spliced if they could get a hoose. The hoose they got has just been described. Lisbeth's mither wis a Fifer, hence her middle name.

When they went to see the minister he ushered the couple into his cosy sitting room and began to ask the necessary questions. 'Ah!' says the good man, 'I know that Buchan is the most common name in this town but this is the first time that I've met both prospective partners with the same surname! Any relationship?'

'Och aye!' says Lisbeth, 'Eance in Yarmouth an' twice at hame!'

Apparently the minister didn't understand.

Well now, the happy pair set about preparing their nestie. It was a fine big room and once it was papered it would look fine! Jeemsie got the len o' a cooper's eetch (adze) and attacked the worst of the knots in the floor, knots which would destroy the new fleer o' canvas (lino).

According to fisher custom 'He' was obliged to provide the bride's claes and a frock for the bridesmaid along wi' a fite sark for the best man. 'He' would be responsible for all expenses of the wedding and 'He' would be obliged to provide all kitchen or living-room furniture.

'She' would provide all the linen and the bedroom furniture. The linen or 'bottom drawer' was always called her 'providin' '.

For a young fisherman of his day Jeemsie was financially well-heeled, for in the Commercial Bank he had £130. Thus he could lash out on a top quality dining-room suite which cost all of £33.

'Afa' gran'.'

Lisbeth managed to provide a decent bedroom suite (£26) then she was completely skint. There was very little to be made in a guttin' yard!

Jeemsie chipped in to help her with one or two items for her widowed mother couldn't afford to assist and when the two turtle doves finally moved in they had behind

Fisher Men in Fisher Rig get the tarry rope aboard at Portknockie. Is that the skipper with the jaunty rake on his bonnet?

Hauling lines on the Viking Bank. Adam Milne shows off a bonny halibut. SD Guiding Light.

Fishwives on Peterhead quay. Probably after herring.

The head of
Peterhead
South Harbour.
Say 100 years
ago? Note the
paddle-tug.

The work-force
in one curing
yard.

A place for the spreading of nets. Now Battery Park, Ives Park and Gadle Braes, Peterhead.

Fifty years on and it's still a race for the Broch.

Let's not forget the kippers! Here Peggy Buchan (Bet's Peggy) carries a 'tentering stick' with eight pairs of kippers.

A lane between the Seagate and the Broadgate, Peterhead. Now the site of a filling station.

Reddin' the sma' line. Before the days of rubber boots. The line is in a wooden 'backet' whose wicker counterpart was a 'scull'.

Buckie quines wait for the fleet at Yarmouth. The wicker-work containers (sweels) each held two baskets of herring and were an outstanding feature of the East Anglian scene.

Sorrow on the Sea.
Olive Branch *PD 77 overwhelmed by broken seas a mile or two off Yarmouth with the loss of nine men including a father and three sons and a father and son on 26th November 1936. Shattered hull drifted ashore next day.*

South Harbour Entrance Peterhead. Say 1930?

Great-lines in their baskets on SD Ephratah *PD 170. Note the rows of hooks stuck into cork. Steam-driven line hauler on the rail.*

A Race for the Broch.
No shelter-decks here, boys! Not even a wheelhouse.

No Room in the Inn.
Peterhead Harbour is choc-a-bloc so drifters use Smith's Embankment,
while vessels in the background lie at anchor!

them a healthy balance of £65. Quite comfortable! Many a young couple didn't have the half of that!

Every stick of furniture the newly weds possessed was arranged in the one room, with the exception of Lisbeth's china cabinet. This had been a present from an aunt who agreed to store it till Lisbeth got mair room. She actually stored it for fourteen years!

You could say the room was a wee bittie congested, but this was commonplace in those days. Very few indeed had two rooms!

So in the one room Jeemsie and Lisbeth cooked, ate, slept and washed! Every drop of fresh water had to be carried in and every drop of slops had to be carried out. Ditto with the coal and the ashes. Every call of nature meant a round trip to the close, often in appalling weather.

Then, when the bairn arrived, her crib was set in front of the window – it could go nowhere else, and the pram had to bide in the washing hoose!

There was no lack of problems. With strong north winds the lum would spew great clouds o' rick into the room an' the gas licht would blink, blink for hours. To stop the rick meant opening the door or the window, then they were frozen!

Visitors usually called at awkward times when Jeemsie was snatching a few hours' sleep. Privacy was an unknown quantity.

Still, in some ways they were fortunate for hundreds of other couples had two or three flights of stairs to contend wi'!

Came the war years when the crib had to be shifted every night so that the 'black-out' – a sheet of stout grey paper on a close fitting wooden frame – could be positioned in the window frame. It certainly made the place warmer but it was oh so depressing.

Then came the fearsome night (one of the many) when Jerry bombed the toon. Jeemsie, hame on leave, was fast asleep when a bomb landed less than a hundred yards away. The 'black-out' flew richt across the room an' the 'hale winda came in in a spleeter o' broken gless. Not a soun' fae the bairn!

In a flash Jeemsie was at the crib, his hert full o' dread, feart to licht his torch, but when his shaky fingers finally switched it on he found the bairn still soun' asleep on the pink silk cushion she had for a pilla.

A' roon the craitur's heid great slivers o' gless had been driven richt throwe the cushion but on the bairn hersel', not a mark!

Jeemsie an' Lisbeth baith said 'Thank You' that nicht!

The crib was never at the window again!

Wis there nivver a lach ava? Jist wyte a meenit noo!

There wis ae nicht that Jeemsie an' Lisbeth got unexpected visitors, an' that meant tay. The folk had jist left fin in comes mair folk, an' that meant mair tay! Ye ken the wye o't. The second lot left for hame in a storm o' win' an' rain, then Jeemsie gied Lisbeth a han' wi' the dishes an' by that time it wis time to turn in for the nicht.

Noo Jeemsie should ha'e geen roon' the back close t' the closet but it wis jist hale watter an' he wis in sark sleeves an' carpets.

'Och!' says he til himsel', 'I've a fine ticht biler so I should be a'richt till mornin'!' So he lay doon an' happet his heid.

But at twa o'clock in the mornin' his biler telt him that, if he didna dee something quick, it wid burst! So oot-ower he scrambled, bare feet on the caul' canvas an' it wis still hale watter!

'Och!' says he again, 'I canna ging oot amon' that! I'll tak' the pail, an' if I keep it quiet she'll nivver ken! She's soun' an' roon' onywye!'

So in the black dark he fichered aboot for the pail which he lifted before makin' a start.

Od! He naear lowpit oot o's sark fin she spoke til 'im oot o' the darkness.

'Fan are ye gaan t' stop? Ye'll ha'e that thing rinnin' ower yet!'

Sheer guilt gart him answer a thochtie sharper than usual: 'Jist 'ee lie doon an' be quaet, quine! There's naething t' get excited aboot! It's nae up t' my thoom yet!'

I spoke to Jeemsie yesterday at the shore. After telling me about the pail he said 'I wis up at my dother's last nicht. Man, ye nivver saw a hoose like it! It's nae canvas noo, but carpets a' wye'. An' the bath-room! Ye wid be feart t' ging intill't. Ye maybe winna believe me, but there's a thing ye can sit on an' scoot het watter at yer ain starn!'

Then as we parted company he remarked.

'Peter, my freen, they dinna ken they're livin'!'

The day Nelson got bitten in a short circus

'Foreigners is a' the same!' says the Turk. 'Ye dinna ha'e t' be coorse t' them, but ye hiv t' be firm wi' them!'

This pearl of wisdom was delivered on a bitterly cold morning in February just prior to the Hitler war as the *Meadowsweet* lay at anchor close to the east side of the May Island in the Firth of Forth.

The previous evening the *Meadowsweet* had shot her fleet of nets about a mile to the south of 'the Mey' in the quest for herring which were, in those days, quite plentiful when the spirit moved them.

On exactly the same errand, a Dyker drifter (from Cellardyke) had executed the same operation three-quarters of a mile further south. Thus both vessels had a good wide berth, but during the night a freak set of the tide had brought the two fleets of nets together in a tangled mess.

The process of separating the fleets was carried out in silence apart from a few uncomplimentary exchanges between the skippers as and when they came within earshot of each other. Since each fleet of nets had 'blinded' the other there were very few herring and it was exasperation rather than anger which fuelled the heated remarks.

As the nets were finally separated the Turk fired his final salvo – 'Ye great ba'-heidit oaf that ye are! Jist 'ee wyte till ye come t' Scotlan'! Syne we'll sort ye!'

The startling reply shook the Turk to the core, for at last he had met a vocabulary even more descriptive than his own!

A hardy breed, the Dykers. For them this inshore herring lark was just a stopgap. With the first hint of spring they would be off to distant waters with their great-lines. The Patch, the Reef and the Viking would be their stamping grounds. Aye! and even the Faroes.

Well, now, since there were no herrings to land, the Turk had elected to drop anchor for the day and the crew were impatient for breakfast, herrings fried as they should be fried.

Here's the recipe: (1) Remove the scales by scraping the fish from tail to head. (2) Remove the head and tail. (3) Split the belly open and remove all contents with the thumb. (4) Wash thoroughly. (5) On each side of the body cut three or four gashes from the back towards the belly taking care not to sever the bone. (6) Dip in oatmeal and fry. On no account should the bone be removed.

Herrings fried in this fashion will give you several juicy 'chunks' from each side, chunks jist the richt size for the fingers! Forks and knives to herrin'? Nivver! That wid be like sacrilege!

But dinna dee fit the Turk did, for aye fin he wis aitin' herrin' he keepit dichtin' his fingers aneth his oxters so that ae washin'-day his wife wis heard to say, 'My man's that fat he swytes grease'!

As a rule the Turk said Grace before meals in his own peculiar way. With his head propped on one hand he would utter a few weird grunts then spit in the stove. The resultant sizzle was the signal for all hands to 'muck in', but when it was a herring breakfast he made an expansive gesture and said, 'We dinna gie thanks for this boys. This is oor ain!'

'I've seen better herrin' mony a time!' says Jeemsie.

'Weel, my loon,' says the skipper, 'They're winter herrin', nae fat, nae ile, nae naething! Jist like tangles! An' forbyes, there's a lot o' affluence fae the factories comes doon this river, an' there's a' the coal-stew fae the mines, so the herrin' couldna be richt!' This from a man who was on his fourth herring made the cook blink!

There was a sudden hush at table when Nelson lifted the tin of Ideal milk and shook it over his plate.

'Dalmichty!' cries Duncan, 'Fit are ye deein', mannie?'

'Oh!' says Nelson, 'I thocht it wis the saat'! Me een's geen a' queer!'

'Control yersel', Duncan' says the Turk 'There's nae need for sweerin'!'

'Fa's sweerin'?' says Duncan 'Dalmichty's nae a bad word! It's a place atween Dalmally an' Dalwhinnie!'

Since the Turk was ignorant on rural things he let the matter drop, but later he consulted Dumplins, the mate, aboot Nelson.

'He's surely as blin' as a bat in his aul' age!' says the Turk.

'Nivver een!' says Dumplins, 'He's due t' retire this 'ear an' he's efter the "Lascar Pension". That's aboot seven an' six the quarter but if he can produce a physical defect he'll maybe get one an' six extra! He's workin' the oracle wi's sicht!'

The Turk could hardly believe his ears. 'For one and six? Fancy!'

In his teens the mate had once been confronted with the picture of a Victorian lady in the low-cut dress of that period. In amazement he had exclaimed, 'Jingers! I winner if this quine kens her dumplins is bilin' ower!' See now how he got the nickname?

Two nights later a sudden south-east gale sent the whole fleet running for shelter. It was impossible to enter any of the small fishing ports because it was low water, a fact which brought headaches to men accustomed to deep-water ports.

'Aye aye!' says the Turk 'In oor pairt o' the country men gets bothered wi' their watter, but down here they're bothered wi' the want o't!'

The nearest deep-water port was Methil whose multitude of lights of all colours, coupled with heavy snow showers, made it very difficult for the Turk's crew to spot the pier-head light. As you might expect it was Nelson who saw it first!

'Aye, aye!' says the Turk again, 'Blin' as a bat, is he? But bats could aye see in the dark!'

Daylight found the big dock at Methil well filled with fishing boats. Cadgers had soon bought up the few herring available and now the only sign of life was butchers' runners canvassing for orders. Their price for top quality fresh meat was 'a shillin' the pun', owerheid'. As Jeemsie said, 'It wis fine chaip roast but gey dear for sassidges'!

A good cook could feed his crew like fighting cocks on ten bob per man per week! What price now?

In the evening both wind and snow had abated somewhat, and several little groups of fishermen could be seen making their way townwards between the lines of coal trucks. A motley, unshaven throng.

'Had there been a horse or twa,' says Jeemsie, 'It wid be like yon picter o' Napoleon's retreat fae Moscow'! All for the sake o' a breath o' air, a stretch o' the laigs an' maybe a baggie o' chips!

'Hold on a meentie, lads' says Nelson, 'I winna be lang'! Then he disappeared into the bowels of one of those ancient, green painted, cast-iron monstrosities which passed as public toilets. Open to the sky they were usually sited where a lamp-post could shine into them.

By jingers, Nelson wisna lang! Five seconds flat an' he wis oot again, howlin' pen-an-ink, an' his ae e'e flashin' like Buchan Ness!

'Fit's adee, Nelson? Hiv ye seen a ghost?' says the Turk.

'No, no!' says Nelson? 'I'd hardly gotten a start fin there wis a great blue flash an' somethin' took a bite o' me'!

'Dalmichty!' says Duncan. 'Nae sweerin'!' says the Turk. 'I'd better get a bobby' says Jeemsie, and he ran off.

Nelson's mates carried him back to the *Meadowsweet* and laid him in his bunk. A few minutes later a dock policeman arrived, accompanied by a doctor who examined the patient in the privacy of the cabin, while the rest of the crew remained on deck. Soon the Turk was summoned to receive the doctor's report which he later repeated to his crew in his own impeccable style.

'Now, boys, Nelson's nae in a gweed wye! He his t' bide in his bed for a day. It seems that lettric wis gettin' fae the lamp-post into the iron water-closet, an' seein' that water conducts lettric, peer Nelson's gotten a lettric shock. I'm thinkin' his fingers is burnt ana'! The doctor says if he hidna been wearin' rubber boots he could ha'e been deid!'

'Dalmichty!' says Duncan. 'Nae sweerin'!' says the Turk.

'Ho-ho-ho!' says Jeemsie. 'I'll bet ye Nelson 'll get a bittie extra on is pension noo!'

An hour or so later Duncan and Jeemsie 'gid up for chips' and as they made their way back their conversation was largely on electrical matters on which they were both ignorant.

'Hey Duncan! The bobby said they wid need t' investigate fit wye there wis a short circus atween the lamp-post an' the urinal. Fit's a short circus, Duncan, an' fit on earth's a urinal?'

'I canna tell ye that my loon! I'm nae a Catholic!'

Tales of the bad landings

Am Balg is the Gaelic name for a rocky islet which lies a scant mile from the coast some half-dozen miles south of Cape Wrath.

The east coast name for the same isle is Bulgie (with a hard 'g') and this name has come to embrace the rich fishing grounds a few miles to the west.

On these grounds the herring shoals were at times so dense that to put a drift net in the water at all was simply to court disaster. Many an east-coaster, in the drifter days, met his Waterloo at Bulgie for only the fortunate few could thole the loss of an entire fleet of nets.

Putting only half the nets in the water was one way of reducing the risk; double bowse (floats) was another method.

Some skippers favoured putting a stopper round the middle of each net as it was run out, thus reducing, by at least half, the fishing area of the net.

And still nets were lost through sheer overweight of fish.

The only guarantee of safety was to keep all the nets in the ship – and starve!

And yet one could shoot a whole fleet of nets at Bulgie every night for weeks and catch precisely nothing!

Today's fisher has no such problem. His wonderful electronic devices can tell him whether or not the fish are there.

He can measure the dimensions of a shoal and its rate of movement; its distance from the bottom and from the surface can be accurately plotted and indeed a practised skipper can, at times, encircle just enough and no more of a shoal for his boat and his crew to handle. Guesswork is largely a thing of the past.

But let's get back to Bulgie in the drifter days.

The *Meadowsweet* (skipper Bob McTurk) had hauled 160 cran and had made for Stornoway on the Isle of Lewis. Eight nets had been completely lost and many more were severely damaged but these wounds, though serious, were not mortal.

Three of the Turk's less-fortunate fellow skippers had lost the lot and had rounded Cape Wrath on their way home with holds completely empty.

So the Turk considered himself rather lucky.

On arrival at Stornoway, however, his heart dropped into his boots, for he found himself at the tail end of a considerable queue of boats waiting to discharge.

There were a few klondykers in Stornoway Loch but they were simply German trawlers and could not cope with huge amounts of herring.

It was already afternoon and there was no prospect of an early discharge. The ruling price in Stornoway that day was fifteen shillings a cran and there was a distinct possibility that late arrivals would find no market for their catches.

Then out of the blue the Turk received a message from his salesman to the effect that: 'A curer mannie in Loch Clash could take 160 cran and would pay seventeen and six a cran. He had waited all day but not a single boat had entered the loch. Would the Turk accept the offer?'

Of course he would accept! One hundred and sixty half crowns was £20 and that was a lot o' siller! So the *Meadowsweet* cast off and headed back across the Minch to Loch Clash only ten miles from where her shot had been netted. What a boon radio would have been!

But misfortune stepped in. As soon as the *Meadowsweet* had cleared Stornoway Loch she was swallowed up in a blinding snowstorm.

All the way across the Minch, the swirling flakes reduced the visibility to less than a hundred yards and the Turk knew that under such conditions and in the approaching dark it would be suicidal to enter Loch Clash.

So there was no alternative but to dodge and keep a sharp look-out.

During the night the blinding snow gave way to more showery conditions and the great flashing light on the Cape was intermittently visible, but not until first light could the Turk find his desired haven.

Now, Loch Clash is not much of a loch at all, but it is the first available shelter for the mariner who has rounded Cape Wrath from the east, and many a drifter man has been thankful for it.

It is more or less a little bay at the entrance to its big sister Loch Inchard and it had, as it still has, a little jetty at whose head there was a curing station.

Across the end of this jetty the *Meadowsweet* was finally moored and the long hard slog of discharging began.

There was no transport available so the herring had to be carried basket by basket up the jetty to the yard then teemed into the farlin where the guttin' quines were waiting for them.

Not a great distance, but if you're clad in boots and oilskins against the weather and if the snow is more than ankle deep, forty yards is far enough, bearing in mind that 160 cran equals 32 tons!

As a concession to the wintry elements, some of the quines had donned hooded oilskin jackets, but some of the younger ones deeming that such attire would simply impede their progress, had pulled on their moggans (home knitted removable sleeves which covered their arms from elbow to wrist).

Only in very cold weather were moggans worn.

Peterheid quines aye wore blue moggans, hence the term 'Bluemogganers'.

But every one of the quines on Clash Pier was as Highland as a peat! All day long they stood there, heads bowed to the snow showers, and their tireless arms never slacking for a moment except for a short tea-break.

Just before dark, the herrings which were as yet ungutted were 'roosed' – very heavily salted into huge wooden vats – to await the daylight of the following day when they too would be gutted and packed in barrels.

By this time the wind had shifted to the north-west and was freshening rapidly, so the *Meadowsweet* left the pier and turned sharp to port into Loch Inchard.

About three quarters of a mile up that loch she turned sharply to port again and entered that haven of havens Loch Safety, a natural harbour if ever there was one.

The name Loch Safety was the name given to Loch Bervie by east-coasters of a byegone day and it would be difficult to make a happier choice of name.

But Loch Safety had one great drawback – it had no pier, so it was anchor drill for the *Meadowsweet's* crew.

Loch Bervie is now a busy fishing port whose fleet is fast outgrowing the landing facilities.

The pier and market space is hopelessly inadequate and it is quite common to see the boats moored 'twelve off' at the weekend, altho' this is to be drastically improved very shortly.

The crews commute to their homes in mini buses, each boat having its own vehicle. These men are mostly from the Moray Firth ports and they never use the name Loch Safety or Loch Bervie; they simply call it Clash.

Every year, in the spring, they have a real 'posh-do' in the Banff Springs Hotel, a 'do' which rejoices in the name 'The Clash Ball'.

But in the drifter days, crews were banished to the Minch for several weeks on end. To go home overland was unknown and the distance by sea was prohibitive.

I once heard of a Moray Firth shippie that came hame fae the Minch efter ten weeks awa'. Fin they cam' t' their hame port (I daurna say fit place) it wis low watter so they couldna get in!

'Ach!' says the skipper, 'If this is the set o't we'd better jist ging awa' back throwe the Firth!'

'Oh father,' says the loon, 'Wid we nae be better to get a clean shift first?'

'Ach! my loon,' says the skipper again, 'Gie yer linner a gweed flap ower the rail an' she'll dee for anither month!'

All that night, the *Meadowsweet* lay snug at anchor while the gale raged among the craggy hills and her tired crew slept like logs.

In the morning, as they gazed on the snow-clad mountains, Jeemsie the cook was heard to remark: 'Good grief skipper, this is surely a foreign land!'

'I'm nae sure if it's foreign or no,' says the Turk. 'But I ken the folkies here has their ain National Anthem! They sing Psalm 121 instead o' "God Save the King"!'

'Psalm 121? Fit dis that say skipper?'

'I to the hills will lift mine eyes,' says the Turk. 'The Lord Himsel' kens there's naething else here t' lift them till!'

Face down waiting for the 'jumpahs'!

I have seen many queer things in my time, and I aye see the queerest things when I dinna ha'e my gun!

But I nearly took a dwam early one morning in Shields when I saw a mannie in a little boatie shovin' a great muckle iron bolt doon a salmon's throat!

'Oho!' says I to mysel'. 'I'd better get some help, for we hiv a nut case here, an' if he's ootrageous, we'll maybe need the bobby!'

So, accompanied by a deckie I boarded the boatie, making all sorts of soothing sounds to calm the poor wretch.

'Come into my treacly oxter an' get a black-sugar kiss! Naebody's gaun t' hurt ye!' I babbled, whereon he lifted his head and looked at me in alarm.

'Mawnin', Peetah, ha'e we bin taken propah poorly the day?' he asked, laying his hand on the haft of a wicked looking knife, whose glint brought me up sharp.

So it turned out that he wasn't a nut case; he was simply trying to preserve his reputation for being the man who caught the heaviest salmon on the Tyne!

Apparently he derived a great deal of pleasure from hearing the fishwives on the quay as they cleaned their fish – 'Oooh, Jessie, come an see what this one's swallowed!' 'Eee! fancy that now Ruby! It's only washers that's in my one's belly!'

The fact that he was swickin' the wifies didn't seem to trouble him in the least, and he came aboard our boat for a joog o' tay, and to see if we had any surplus lead sinkers. It might allay suspicion if he varied the salmon's diet!

I had a lang news with this old codger and learned that from time immemorial, it had been the legal right of Northumberland fishermen to catch salmon with drift nets.

There was of course a close season when the use of nets was forbidden, but even then some enterprising lads just let their boaties drift aimlessly with the tide.

Apparently they lay flat in the bottom of the open boat keeping dead quiet and the chances were that a 'jumpah' would land in the boat. They might be like that a whole night and nivver see a face, but it was quite possible to get four or five bonny fish for a night's work.

The best place for this caper was close outside the breakers along the beach, if you had the nerve to let a boat drift there.

It was policy to lie face down in the boat because a 25lb salmon dropping from a height of six feet could gie ye a gey sair face. Since the 'jumpahs' had 'lowpit in ower' uninvited, the fishers could not be prosecuted!

My boundless admiration for this old fellow was tinged with not a little envy for at last I had met a bigger and better liar than myself! But when I checked and rechecked the old tale I discovered that it was the truth.

Thereafter I made careful enquiries to see if it was permissible for Scotch (not Scots) fishermen to catch salmon with drift nets, and discovered to my amazement that there was no law against it.

Fancy that now! Generations of fishermen had been brought up to believe that to utter the word 'salmon' was to incur all sorts of misfortune. And to actually handle a salmon was to invite an affliction called the 'Fite Swallin' ' which would affect our bowels to such an extent that we would have to wear kilts, for in no way would there be time to take trousers down!

Aye willin' to try something new, we bought some salmon drift nets and launched into a venture which brought limited success. We found the salmon to be as elusive as the herring; we also learned that a calm night would be a fruitless night and that the real truth was 'the more wind, the more fish'!

When we got home to Peterhead with our new nets, we caused a sensation. We would get the jile, that was sure! But nobody said 'Boo' and we just carried on.

That was how the salmon fishing (drift net) came to the north-east. Others were quick to copy and soon there were salmon nets all over the place, but still salmon were a scarce crap.

The truth is that the salmon drift nets killed more birds than fish! Yon black-and-white birdies that the loons used to call 'marrots' (Gulliemots?) were trapped in the nets when they made their shallow dive and it gave us sair herts to see so many of them drowned.

But nobody was interested in the birdies! They could be slaughtered by the million, so long as the salmon were not molested!

Now let me tell you a story!

'Twas the kind of night that one doesn't easily forget. A few boats had left Peterhead to punch their way round Buchan Ness towards the comparatively calmer waters nearer Girdleness, but one by one they had given up and gone home leaving one solitary craft to brave the gale.

It was not our usual to be 'the only boat on the sea' but it was so that night.

About two miles of the Ythan estuary, we shot our nets and dodged at them for several hours. There was no sleep for anyone, so chaotic was the 'raivelt' motion, but eventually we got the nets aboard and made for home with a score of lovely fish.

When we reached harbour, we hauled the whole fleet of nets on to the pier because they resembled a rope with corks on it rather than nets.

These salmon nets had an unhappy knack of rowin' themselves up so that the yarn got all twisted up with the cork rope, and that in a thousand different ways. The job of taking the twists out so that the net could be freed from the rope, required infinite patience and a lot of time. It could not be done by mittened hands.

The wind had veered northerly with flurries of snow and it was bitterly cold.

Daylight was just breaking when a beautiful Bentley drew up on the pier beside us. Therein sat a little wee mannie wi' a gamekeepers' hat, festooned with trout flies.

The chauffeur sat like a statue while the mannikie opened a window to ask: 'Have you been at sea, chaps?'

Oh aye! We had been at sea!

'Have you caught any salmon chaps?'

Oh aye! We had some!

'Which one of you is skipper, chaps?'

'It's me,' says I. 'Are ye lost, or something, that ye're doon here at this time o' the mornin'? Respectable folk's still in their beds ye ken!'

He agreed readily, then he told me a strange tale.

The previous evening, before dark, he had been at Arbroath seeking a salmon, but no boats were at sea.

He had been about to return home when a fisherman told him that Peter o' the *Twinklin' Star* was at sea; he had heard him on the wireless.

And where would he find this Peter?

Up in Peterheid, of course.

So the great Bentley drove northward, calling at every village on the way in a fruitless search for a salmon. Not even Port Errol and Boddam had been overlooked, but now he had some hopes of success.

Could he see our fish?

Certainly! But he would need to come out of the car!

He stood agape at the sight of the beauties which glistened like silver on the deck. In a mere whisper he asked: 'Can I have one? Please!'

'Aye, surely,' says I, 'but ye'll ha'e to pey for't. Naebody gets a fry o' salmon!'

He was more than willing to pay. And when he had picked the biggest fish I said: 'That'll be ten bob the pun' an' she's aboot twinty pun'!'

No trouble at all to an exceedingly well filled wallet. With great reverence he laid the fish in the boot of the car. The chauffeur was not allowed to touch it!

Then, hesitantly, he asked: 'Could I have another, please?'

'Aye! Surely. Ye can tak' the lot as lang's ye've siller!'

Just then 'Willicks' appeared on the scene. He was for several years in the Caley shop and was always needlessly early on the job.

'Hey!' says I to the mannie. 'We can wye the fish if ye like! I widna sleep if I'd cheated ye!'

So the two beauties were duly weighed, 21 and 19lbs apiece. Forty pun' at ten bob – £20.

Oh, he wis pleased! While he was washing his hands, I asked the chauffeur to tell me fa the mannie wis.

This he refused to do, but he would tell me why the need for the salmon was so urgent.

The mannie had two sons who went fishing for trout with their dad. They had been at it off and on for a year, and the peer sowl hadna catched a fish yet!

The boys, however, had baith a little trootie or two to their credit and they just made a feel o' their father.

But this mornin' he wid let them see the wye! He wid march up the drive to the mansion wi' a great muckle fish in ilka han'! That wid shut them up!

No job for a volunteer

At the tender age of fourteen Kitty was in the curing yard gutting herring. With two of her former classmates she had taken up the traditional occupation of the fisher quines, and now the trio formed a 'crew o' learners'.

There were always three to a crew, two gutters and a packer, and their uniform comprised an oilskin skirt and a bib, and a pair o' toppers (rubber boots).

Their headgear was a cotton muffler and on the upper parts of their bodies they wore a fisherman's jersey with sleeves only to the elbow, or even an old cotton blouse. As protection against the 'coorse saat' (rough salt) with which the herrings were liberally clarted, the quines' fingers were rowed in 'clooties', strips of cloth wrapped tightly round each finger and secured with cotton thread.

The gutter's tool was a 'futtle', a short, stubby gutting knife with a fixed blade; the packer's tool was a shallow circular metal scoop polished like silver by the abrasive saat.

In a curing yard there could be anything from four to ten crews of women, depending on the status of the curer. Immediately prior to the start of the herring season the curer would give each crew member her 'arles', sometimes as much as £1, and this was an unwritten, seldom broken contract for the whole of that season, the recipient would gut herring for that curer as and when required, rain or shine.

The rate of pay would be 'a shillin' the barrel' per crew, so for each barrel of herring which any crew gutted each quine got fourpence! Work that out at an average of 750 herring to a barrel! How much per herring?

The ages of the quines varied from 14 to 65. Fancy bein' a 'quine' at pension age! The packer had to be good for she had to keep pace with two women's gutting and without fail the packer was the crew's cashier or treasurer. Kitty was a packer.

Now, the salting of the herring actually began at the quayside. Not until the late 1940s did the herring drifters carry boxes . . . and even then the number of boxes carried was strictly limited. The catch was always in bulk and was swung ashore one basket at a time.

Two deckies would grasp the swinging basket and empty the contents into a 'kit', a container provided by the curer for the transport of the catch to the curing yard. A kit held one basket, or seven stone of herring and it must be clearly understood that the kit was not a barrel, although it was made by local coopers.

The kit had the same shape as a glass tumbler and empty kits could be stowed just like tumblers, one inside the other. See?

While the herring poured like quicksilver from the basket to the kit, a cooper would dose them liberally with salt from a barrel, using the same metal scoop that the packers used, then he would tilt the kit and 'rowe' it aside only to replace it with an empty one ready for the next basket. The salt took the slipperiness from the fish making them much more easy to handle when the quines got them.

Four baskets or four kits made one cran. The salt itself was of Spanish, Italian or Sardinian origin and was like coarse gravel. It was also of a dazzling whiteness.

On motor lorries or on long flat carts the kits of herring were taken to the curing yard.

On the stage which had to be of great strength the kits of herring were stowed ready to fill the 'farlin', a wooden trough whose bottom sloped downwards towards the front. The farlin was as long as the stage and along its front stood the row of guttin' quines in their oilskin cwites (skirts).

When the farlin had been filled with herring the gaffer would give the signal to start gutting. Since the quines were all on piece-work 'startin' afore yer neeper' was strictly forbidden.

In front of her and a wee bittie to the side each gutter had a small wooden tub or 'coggie' to receive the herring guts, and behind her she would have at least three shallow wooden tubs to catch the gutted fish in three selections, full, matt-full and small. The tubs had iron carrying-handles and were extremely heavy.

To see a practised gutter at her task was to see skill of the very highest order. Two swift jabs of the futtle removed the gills and the gut, a flick of the wrist sent the offal into the coggie and a deft movement of the left hand sent the gutted fish into its appropriate tub. There was no looking behind them, yet very few fish missed their appointed tub. The very speed of the quines' hands was amazing.

As soon as a few tubs were filled the three quines carried them outside and emptied them into a roosin'-box, a wooden container about four feet square and eighteen inches deep which stood on four legs. In this container the packer turned the herrin' ower wi' her scoop and gave them an extra dusting of salt as required before starting to pack them in a barrel, heads outward, bellies up.

Using both hands she would lift several herring from the box and pack them neatly in the bottom of the barrel. When the first tier or 'boddim' had been laid she would yell for the gaffer to come and inspect it. Not until he was satisfied was she allowed to carry on packing, then her fingers would fly.

Tier after tier of herring, scoop after scoop of salt. It was hot, hard work leaning into the very bottom of the barrel but naturally things got easier as the barrel filled up. Not that the job was ever easy.

For a summer or twa I was 'the loon' in a curing yard.

It was hard, healthy work which I really enjoyed especially since the stage and the farlin were in the open air. This was quite common. Sometimes when the quines were working late I would light paraffin flares or bubblies which were the only illumination.

It was all something of an adventure to a loon but the quines must have been ready to drop. 'Ramona' and 'South of the Border' were favourite songs with the younger women, but oh, when the Hielan' deems sang their mournful Gaelic airs everything seemed so eerie it gart me shiver. . .

Een o' my jobbies as orra loon wis t' gie the quines their pey. If there wis nae herrin' on pey-day I took the pey packet t' the packer's hoose. If the yard wis busy the packer got her envelopie at her wark.

I thocht this wis daft. Fit wis the peer quine supposed t' dee wi' a pey packet an' her wearin' a cwite athoot pooches, her fingers rowed in cloots an' hersel' clartit wi' gour?

The first time I gied Kitty her packet she grat like a bairn 'cos the amount pencilled on the ootside wis jist pathetic. I left her greetin' an' passed t' the next quine. Belle wis busy in the boddim o' the barrel so I could see her form fae the waist doon only, but fin I gied her sonsie hip a clap she cam' oot o' the barrel like a jake-in-the-box. Then she wis worth seein'!

My private name for her wis 'The Busty Bombshell' an' I'm sure I wis in love wi' her at that time, tho' she widna look at a loon like me 'cos she was eichteen an' I wis twa 'ear younger.

'Hey Belle,' says I, lookin' at her in silent worship, 'Here's yer pey packet'!

'Ooh, that's fine! But far am I supposed t' keep it?'

'That's up to you,' says I, preparin' t' move t' the neist packer.

'Wyte a meenit!' says Belle, an' stoppin' a wee bittie in my direction she fluttered her bonny lashes towards her copious cleavage (I think that's the richt word).

'Pit the packetie doon there, my loon!'

'Me? Doon there? Nae fear! That wid be rude! My mither wid be reid mad!'

'Nivver mind yer mither, ye gowk; she winna ken. An' forbyes ye're jist a gweed-faced innocent loon yet! Go on!'

So I stuck the packetie in the bonny letter-box.

'That's nae eese!' she says, 'Shiv the thing hine doon or I'll loss't in the boddim o' the barrel, an' that widna dee!'

Oh boys-o-boys! Oh my govies! Spik aboot clootie dumplins? I'll sweer she didna loss yon packetie in the barrel!

Three weeks later I was on the same job again. Kitty didna greet this time – the young quines wis learnin' fast!

Then I came to Belle. 'Aye aye, Belle! Will I pit yer pey far I pit it last time?'

'Awyte, no!' says she, wi' her cheeks like fire, 'Ye'll dee nae sic thing!'

'Foo nae? says I.

''Cos I had t' tirr afore I could get my pey yon day! Ye're nae near sic a gweed-faced innocent loon as I thocht, ye coorse vratch!'

Fancy her sayin' a thing like that fin I was jist thinkin' that a volunteer wid dee the job far better than ony pressed man!

Working on a fool, watery brute!

Towards the end of World War I, the 'Government' saw fit to order a fleet of drifters for use as 'sweepers, tenders, etc. These shippies were to be of a standard design and the building of them was farmed out to several yards all over the country.

But although the design was standard it was quite easy for an expert to spot superficial differences which betrayed their yard of origin, and by an 'expert' I mean a fisher loon who could tell you a shippies' name when all that was visible in the distance was the smoke from the funnel!

The iron 'standard boats' were grand craft when punching into a head wind, but otherwise they were 'fool, watery brutes'. The wooden members of the species were good all-rounders.

During World War II, the 'Government' saw fit to build a fleet of motor boats (MFVs), again of standard design, and again it was easy to spot a Geordie Forbes from a Herd and McKenzie or an Irvin. These boats came in three sizes – 50 ft., 65 ft. and 75 ft., powered by 66 h.p. Kelvins, 88 h.p. Kelvins and 150 h.p. Lister Blackstone engines respectively.

There was also a bigger, 90 ft. version which was built for fire fighting but they were not popular with fishermen after the war. The most popular as far as fishermen were concerned were the 65 ft. and 75 ft. vessels which proved very adaptable as dual-purpose craft, i.e. for herring or white fish.

I was in a 75-footer for a few years and found her to be quite a good boat apart from one or two glaring faults.

She, like all the others, had been built for the Navy, so there had to be accommodation for officers. Consequently she had a deck house like a block of flats surmounted by a dirty great funnel.

The Navy always thinks that there's plenty o' room up the wye!

When lying head to wind at the herring nets she wouldn't lie like a Christian at all, but did her best to roll our guts out!

Conversely she was a marvel broadside on!

But all these boats had a most annoying fault! The propellor made a terrific racket fit to scare the verra flechs aff ye! The noise in the cabin was like steens on a corrugated roof and although several 'cures' were attempted none proved effective.

I was 'driver' of a 150 h.p. Blackstone for a few years and thus came to know every nut and bolt in the fool, stinkin' beast and again, thereby hangs a tale.

It came to pass, in the fullness of time (i.e. when I had managed to rake a few pounds thegither) that I decided that it was time we had a bathroom in the house.

At that time I was bidin' in the old fisher district, the Roanheads, where bathrooms were almost unknown – as was the case in most of the town!

I was getting rather tired of having to leave a warm fireside to go and sit in an outside toilet which, in winter, could have passed as a fridge.

'What will the robin do then, poor thing?' was a childhood phrase which seemed to come to mind rather too often. So I ups and goes through the official channels for permission which was readily given, but I didna get a 'grunt' (the Peterhead word for grant).

The only grunt I got wis fae the wife because I started to demolish the inside of the house on a Saturday afternoon. The good woman should have been christened Charity, for charity suffereth long and is kind!

In the course of this demolition I discovered some little holies in one or two jeests so I consulted a friend of long standing. After expert examination he announced 'Och! that's widworm! But it's nae bad! I ken widworm fin I see't. Ye see, I've been thirty 'ear wi' the Cooncil!'

My observation that that wis a lang time to be idle didn't seem to ruffle him at all. His advice was to get a suppie diesel ile an' pit it on the timmer. It wid stink for a fylie but it wid certainly kill the beasties!

Now, to get a suppie diesel was no problem! All I had to do was to take a tin down to the boat where I could fill it from the tank. So next afternoon I set off gaily with a gallon tin to procure the needful but I had only got a third of the distance when it started to rain very heavily, forcing me to seek shelter.

The nearest refuge was the open galley door of a fishing boat near the slipway, a stranger who had come to Peterhead for refit. This was nothing new because in my youth the drifters from Cellardyke came all the way to Peterhead for a new funnel. I had just got into the galley when I collided with two fitters who had just come up from the engine room.

'Hi, Peter,' says one of them, 'if ye're bidin' here a whilie, will ye keep an eye on our spanners? We're awa' for wir tay an' there's an affa lot o' thiefs aboot the place!

'We've left the engine runnin' – she's ready to go! If the crew comes for the boat jist gar them wyte till we come back!'

I immediately made for the engine-room which was identical to the one I'd had years before. This was a 75 ft. MFV and the newly overhauled Blackstone was ticking over like a clockie.

For a few minutes I revelled in nostalgia, the old familiar sounds and smells. I revved and slowed the engine, fichered wi' this and that and then I spotted the fuel service tank above my head. Boys, here was diesel a-plenty, ready to hand! I could fill my tinnie here and nobody would ever know.

Conscience began to chirp in my lug, but I couldna hear for the dirl o' the engine. And besides, it wis only a wee suppie and it wis hale watter and my ain boatie wis hine awa' and I wis gardin' ither folk's spanners fae thiefs and it wis force ten increasing to force twelve and if I didna tak' it noo I needna bother!

So up went the tin and down came the drain-cock valve and diesel began to flow. The tin was about a quarter full when I spied on the ladder a pair of highly-polished shoes, then a pair of beautifully-tailored trousers followed by an immaculate suede jacket. Finally I saw the whole man, a well-built chiel wi' clear blue een, and a fine smell o' Brut.

'Hi, skipper!' says I, 'Fit like?'

'Nae bad, nae bad,' says he, eyeing my tin. 'Are 'ee an engineer? Nivver saw you afore!'

'Och aye, been an engineer since I left the school!' which in a sense was strictly true.

'Fit are ye deein' wi' that tin?'

'I'm jist checkin' to see that there's nae water in yer tank. It widna dee to ha'e ye lyin' stoppit ootside wi' water in yer fuel.'

'Nivver saw that deen afore,' says he. 'Ye maun be affa parteeclar!'

'Na, na,' says I, 'ye're better to dee the job richt! I aye dee this!'

It was standard practice to drain off a drappie regularly. No doubt his own chief did so, although the skipper hadn't seen him at it. Skippers are out of their element in the engine-room, as a rule.

He asked a few more questions then looking at the donkey pump (i.e. the pump for the hose) he said: 'I hope ye've sorted that pump! I could pee faster than that thing!'

Since that wasn't a question it required no answer but I did ask him civilly whether he was complaining about the pump or bragging about himself. That made him laugh and as he made to climb the ladder he said: 'Ye're an affa lad! My crew's in the Mission for a fly-cup; I'm awa' to the office an' fin I come back I'll see that ye get something t' yersel' for mindin' on that tank!'

Halfway up the trap he paused and said: 'Fit wye did 'ee ken I wis the skipper?'

'Man,' says I, 'there's something aboot ye that canna be misteen! Ye fairly look the pairt. Ye jist radiate confidence and assurance! Something a boddy could lippen till!'

'Ye could be richt, freen,' says he, nodding his head sagely, 'I'm nae feel, tho' I fart in the Kirk'!

I didn't have the nerve to tell him that he wis far ower fat to be a deckie, far ower clean to be a chief an' far ower bonny dressed to be a cook.

To the fitters, returned from their tay, I reported that I hidna seen nae thiefs but I had seen the skipper who was to bring something to mysel', a something the fitters could share between them, for I was going home.

When I learned later that the 'something' had not materialised, I reflected sadly as I splashed the mannie's diesel on my timmer that 'the Jews is nae a' in Jerusalem'!

A lesson in true kindliness

I derive a great deal of pleasure from the fact that, as I grow steadily older, my boyhood years, my special years, become ever more vividly clear in my memory.

Important dates and events of the intervening years may at times be shrouded in a soft haze, yet the most distant days of all still retain the beauty and the freshness of a dream.

The characters who flitted across the stage of my earliest years were mostly old people, but then, to a little boy the greater part of the world's population is old.

Of course I had a veritable host of playmates whom I remember with affection, in spite of the fact that some of them were downright 'coorse'.

But it was the old folk, the real old timers that I remember most fondly for there was a something about them which I can only describe as kindness; not that these folks had anything to give. On the contrary, they had very, very little!

But then kindness, or kindliness, the bonniest word in the English language is not necessarily involved with actual giving unless it be the giving of oneself. No, it is a far deeper word than that.

But enough of sermonising! Let me tell you about Cephas, one of my really favourite people!

Cephas was a gentleman, and by that I mean he really was a gentle man. That he was old I had no doubt.

That he was well read I was perfectly sure, for when Cephas used the English language, of which he was very fond, there were no double negatives, no split infinitives, no misrelated participles!

When Cephas 'talked' (i.e. spoke in English) he was a joy to listen to.

He could discourse quite freely on several subjects, and on the Scriptures in particular, not in any dogmatic, Hellfire-and-damnation manner, but in a sweet persuasiveness that portrayed the love of God as being broader than the measure of man's mind. His theology did not suit everybody, but I loved it, young as I was.

Cephas could be very pleasant company indeed, but oh boys he wis fool! He wis jist fair yirdit. His acquaintance

with soap and water could only be described as the nodding variety!

Some of my elder companions took great pleasure in relating the story of how poor Cephas had once been stricken by a sudden and serious malady which decreed that he should be 'rushed awa' t' Aiberdeen!'

There, the ward sister, a proper stickler fae the Garmond was adamant that no such person could be 'beddit athoot a bath!'

The upshot was that they gied Cephas three waters, then they got 'is sark! Ye ken, I never really believed that story!

Cephas was not, and apparently never had been a man of action. All his days he had loved to stray into bypath meadow from whence he would watch the world go by.

He had a little boat which had no engine and in this frail craft he purported to be a fisherman, never more than half a mile from shore and not even there unless it was flat calm!

Cephas always addressed my father as 'Cousin', a relationship which my father would vigorously deny!

For my father, Cephas had the greatest respect, and while my father certainly admired the intelligence of his professed 'Cousin' he had no time for the old man's way of life. The two were as different as chalk and cheese!

I remember particularly well one day when my Da had just arrived home from Yarmouth. The nets had been taken ashore and hung on fences to dry. Each member of the crew had his whole barrel or 'halfie' of salt herring delivered to his home and now that it was dark each man was at hame for his supper wi' his wife an' bairns.

In our house, that meant that father and one son had returned from the sea while three others, a son and two daughters would be home in a few days from the shore side of the herring trade.

The three remaining members of the family, not old enough to leave school had gotten our Yarmouth presents and we were awaiting our tea. But surely Ma was on the slow side the nicht!

Then I remembered! This was the night that Cephas

would call! And, sure enough, he announced his arrival by knocking gently on the door, which I opened to admit the old man.

Immediately on entering he removed his battered bowler hat (not a cheese-cutter) and greeted my father warmly.

'Eh! Cousin! It's fine t' see ye safe hame! Oh! It's supper time wi' ye? Weel I'd better awa' hame an' come back some ither time!

'It's nae richt o' me! I should ha'e kent better! Weel! Seein' that ye insist I'll tak' a bite wi' ye, but jist a bite noo, jist a bite!'

And he took his place at table, a place which had been set for him some time ago.

Strange how the old man's visits always coincided with my father's arrival from Yarmouth!

Once we were all seated, my mother served us liberal helpings of skirly, a great favourite with us! The smell of 'oatmeal an' ingins' sizzling in the pan – sheer delight!

At once Cephas propped his head on his left hand and launched into a Grace which would have taken high honours in the Dimbleby Lecture programme.

Beginning with Moses in the bulrushes, he accompanied the children of Israel on their escape from Egypt. Then, as soon as the Israelites had crossed the Red Sea my mother reached for Cephas' untouched plate and set it on the bink (hob) to keep it warm.

Sensing, rather than hearing this movement I opened my eyes to see my father quietly getting on with his supper. On catching my questioning gaze he indicated that we should all follow suit, but as quietly as possible, which we did, in dead silence. It wis like a 'dummy's meetin' '.

The old man 'didna think muckle o' David tho', mind ye, Solomon wis a hantle waur, wi' a' yon weemin'!

Hop step and jump we were led through the Old Testament until, in Ezekiel's valley of dry bones, Cephas faltered a bittie.

Thereupon my mother, using the corner of her spotless apron lifted the sizzling plate from the bink and set it aneth Cephas' nose. This brought a rather abrupt 'Amen!' and the old boy set to with a will.

Then, having cleared his plate in splendid fashion, sink

me if he didna set oot on anither Grace fit t' beat the first een!

This time he began in the Acts of the Apostles an' wydit thro' the Epistles until he seemed to get bogged down in the Predestination portion of Ephesians.

Then my father who had been leisurely filling his pipe laid his open tobacco pouch in front of Cephas who drew to a close with 'odours of Edom and incense Divine'. It was actually 'Digger Flake'.

Boys! Yon finger fairly kent the wye to teem a pooch an' fill a pipe! I saw my father's e'en widen in mock alarm at the capacity of Cephas' old briar.

Then, between puffs, the old boy declared that Providence had led him here the nicht. Oh aye! He wid fairly tak' a bile o' saut herrin', but the barrel widna be open yet surely!

It wis? Gran'! Oh, aye! He had something t' tak' them hame in, a puddin' dish! Far wis't? Jist ootside the door! Providence again! Boys, yon wis nivver a puddin' dish – ye could ha'e batht a bairn in 't!

When Cephas finally departed my father says 'Is't a 'hale 'ear since he was here last?'

'Oh aye, Andra, it's a 'hale 'ear, but it seems like yestreen!'

'He wis on a different text the nicht, lass! A clivver mannie yon!'

'Fit ither could he be? He is a cousin o' yours, isn't he?' says my mither. She fairly kent the wye t' torment my Da!

'Aye!' says she. 'Providence led Cephas here the nicht an' Providence 'll guide him t' some ither 'Cousin' the morn, an' the day after! Cephas has a lot o' cousins!'

During my last conversation with Cephas he produced a gem which lingers in my memory yet. 'Peter my loon,' says he 'I hiv a lot o' freens, an' freens is jist like fiddle strings – ye darna screw them ower ticht!'

Finally brethren (I learned that fae Cephas) what was Cephas' name when he 'bedd' in your village?

I'm sure ye kent the peer aul' sowl when there was no Welfare State, dependent to a marked degree on the kindliness of 'cousins'.

Wis he a cousin o' yours? Wis 'ee ivver a cousin t' him?

And div ye nae think, as I think, that 'kindliness' is the bonniest word in ony language?

Once upon a time at a mendin'

There was a period in my life when the magic words, 'Once upon a time' were a sure-fire guarantee that the story which followed would be a really good one.

In fancy I would be borne along paths of mystery and wonder, through a land of light and song where no-one wept except the willow, and where in the end everybody lived, happily ever after.

I was finally convinced that the Land of Once Upon a Time had no stable foundation, by a rather salutory experience.

You see, I had read in a bookie about a loon that got a thripenny-bit fae an aul' wifie in the street just 'cos his cheery smile had brightened her day!

'Oho!' says I to mysel' 'It's me for the thripenny-bits! Nae bother ava!'

So I positioned myself at the door of Lipton's shop on the Broadgate (now Ronnie Gordon's furniture shop) and there I bestowed on the world in general, and on aul' wifies in particular, the most dazzling smile you ever saw.

Great were the multitudes that thronged the street for streaky bacon was fourpence the quarter, but nobody paid any heed to the threadbare, poverty-stricken loon wi' the radiant smile! Not a copper!

I'm tellin' ye, if ye smile for three solid hours ye'll ha'e a sair face! At last there came towards me two vaguely familiar faces so in a last despairing effort I 'streetched my mou' fae ear t' lug' but to no avail!

'Good grief! Fa on earth's that?' says wifie number one.

'Oh!' says number two, 'that's een o' Jeannie Mother-well's, but he's nae jist affa richt, 'at een!'

Oh boys! I came doon t' earth wi' a richt clyte yon day! This is a richt hard world, an' it's a sair fecht! Once upon a time? Tell that to somebody else.

Well now, once upon a time (are ye listenin'?) I wis a barfit loon makkin' for the shore fin I met an aul' fisherman, tall an' as stracht as a rash.

He wore a sleeved weskit abeen his navy blue ganjie an' roon' his neck a black silk muffler. On his heid a cheese-cutter an' on his feet a pair o' saft leather ankle-boots. Ye ken him, divn't ye?

'Hey, ma loon!' says he, 'fa echts, you? Fa's your mither?'

Now I kent better than to say Mrs Buchan for at that time every second wifie was a Mrs Buchan so I simply said: 'I'm een o' Jeannie Motherwell's!'

'Weel noo,' says he, 'Ging an' tell Jeannie Motherwell that she'll be nott this aifterneen on the Embankment an' tell her to bring her mennin' needles!' Then seeing anither wifie across the street he cried: 'Hey, Mary! I'm seekin' t' speak t' ye!'

My mother's maiden name was Motherwell, and it amused her that maist o' the fisher folk thocht it was a bye-name. She was an incomer. Fit ither could she be wi' a name like that?

When I brought the old fisherman's message my mother said 'There's surely something far wrang the day! Rin doon the shore an' see fit news ye get!' The news I got was bad indeed!

At the very peak of the summer herring season two of the local herring drifters had met with disaster! Every net they had shot the previous evening had been torn to shreds by 'muldoans'.

Some folk, said that the proper name for 'muldoan' was killer whale. Others said it was a basking shark while yet another group said it was a beast as big as a whale with a fin as big as a sail on its back. A sail-fish, they called it!

Well, whatever their proper name might be, the brutes had destroyed two fleets of nets, each a mile long. They had gone in through one net and out through the next one like skiers doing a slalom!

Not one single net had they missed and by some weird mischance they had picked upon the gear belonging to those who were least able to sustain such a loss.

Since it was the summer season, only the best nets would be in use. Any spare nets the unfortunate fishermen might have had would be older, harder nets suitable for Yarmouth but useless in the summertime.

As the two crews bundled the shattered nets there was much head-shaking among the curious bystanders.

'They'd be jist as weel ti' tie the boats up noo! Afore they get that lot sorted oot the fishin' 'll be feenished! That's supposin' they get them sorted ava!'

And they were quite right; it would take months for these men and their wives to repair the awful damage. A long tear in a net was a comparatively simple job as long as the yarn (meshes) was still there but the great monsters had riven great skelps o' yarn oot o' the nets.

A vast amount of 'patch' would be required and nobody could possibly have that amount, especially since the patch would need to be of the same quality as the nets. So, alas, it was the end of the road!

But Sonnie, wi' the sleeved weskit an' cheese-cutter caip had other ideas, so he set out on a recruiting campaign among the fisher folk.

'Come doon an' bring your mennin' needles. An' a hank or two o' twine wid be a help!' As if by magic the message seemed to preceed him and in a very short time 'the hale toon kent'.

Now then, that afternoon on the Embankment a fair-sized crowd of men, women and youngsters could be seen working at a heap of nets.

The men, mostly elderly, would spread out a net for inspection and if the net was simply torn, it would be passed to the women for mending.

But most of the nets required extensive patches so two nets which proved to be beyond repair were cannibalised to provide patches for nets less badly damaged. Patching was for men, mending was for women.

Youngsters could fill needles with twine or they could keep the yarn of a net tight so that a skilled hand could trim a hole to receive a patch. There was work aplenty for all hands.

Some women sent word that they couldn't come because they were gutting, but they would join the fray as soon as they could; others said they 'couldna leave their bairns but if somebody wid tak' a torn net up to the hoose, they wid dee't at hame!'

A fine jobbie for a loon wi' a barra!

Gnarled old hands which hadn't handled a net for years soon rediscovered their lost skills with needle and knife and the women's fingers altho' unaccustomed to wet yarn flew like the shuttles of a loom. Sonnie was the gaffer; no dispute about that!

In the evening Sonnie took me and my chum aside: 'Tak' that barra an' ging ower t' the Ronheids. Ye'll see a puckle folk workin' there. Look for a mannie, like me b' the name o' Buller an' tell 'im that I'm rinnin' oot o' patch. He'll maybe gie ye a net or twa t' tak back!'

Full of our own importance we set out on our mission, but when we got to the Ronheids we got a shock!

The grassy braes aside the killin' hoose (abattoir) wis black wi' folk. Nets were spread a' wye an' ilka een that could dee onything wi' a net wis up t' the een wi' wark!

Since the crews who owned the nets lived mostly on the north side of the town, most of the damaged gear had been taken there for repair. Apparently Sonnie had 'just gotten a puckly t' sort'.

I had never seen anything like this before. It was great fun for loons to be in the thick of such a throng, 'an' yet there was a something aboot it that wid gar ye greet'!

There was no singing, no daffery; there was instead an almost tangible air of dour determination.

No-one called a halt till well after sunset and several were back on the job at the crack o' dawn. Women came and went as their other duties required, one taking on where another had left off.

Slowly, slowly the tally of nets 'ready for sea' mounted. Twice did my chum and I go back wi' the barra for 'mair nets to sort', and at the end of the third day the task was completed.

Both fleets of nets were ready, somewhat depleted in numbers of course (it could not be otherwise), but the two ships could carry on fishing.

The impossible had been achieved. I'm relying solely on memory and I'm thinkin' that it should have been properly recorded at the time, because such an achievement is worth a place in any book of records.

There have been no herring nets for many years now! The deft fingers which spent so many hours plying the needles are 'a thing of the past'. Fishermen's wives of today do no net-mending.

'Ah!' you may ask. 'But is not the community spirit of former days still alive?'

Well now, in answer to that, I must confess that I'm some like Robbie Burns: 'I guess and fear!'

The Turk gets a bite

The good ship *Meadowsweet* had been designed for work on the open sea, and yet, here she was in the calm and tranquil waters of Loch Glendhu, some four miles inland from the ferry at Kylesku!

Richt into the hert o' the hills! An' fit wid the Turk be seekin' here? Surely nae a load o' peats?

'Dinna be daft!' says the Turk. 'I'm seekin' herrin' bait for my great-lines, 'cos lines athoot bait's as muckle eese as guns athoot ammunition! There's nae a herrin' to be gotten in the Minch so we maun look for the craiturs some ither wye.

'I've seen the herrin' that thick in here that ye could verra near traivel across the loch on them; but I'll be pleased to see a baitin', a basket or twa!'

Now the great-line is completely different from the sma-line in many ways. It is 'gryte' (big) where its junior is 'sma'. Its massive hooks and heavy cordage are for big fish such as halibut, skate and cod in deep waters where a sma-line could never take the strain, and furthermore the great-line was not for baiting in the hoose! No!

It had to be baited while it was being 'shot' or run out of its basket while the ship was underway.

The great-line basket has approximately twice the capacity of a herring basket. One half of the rim, from handle to handle is tightly bound with strong hempen cord to give strength and protection to the wicker-work.

On the opposite half of the rim from handle to handle there is a length of cork about 1½ inches wide and 1 inch thick; this also is firmly secured to the basket.

Now, before you coil the line into the basket it is essential that the end is left hanging over the rim.

On no account must it be left in the bottom of the basket!

Then you can 'redd' the line neatly into the basket sticking each hook in turn into the cork keeping them very close together for you have to stick about 120 hooks into the cork.

It is mandatory that the hooks be 'staggered' in strict rotation, one out and one in so that when the basket is full of line there will be two rows of hooks in the cork, each hook with its 'tail' inside (never outside) the basket.

Then you'll take the end which is hanging over the rim and hitch it loosely to the other end and lay the big knot or the 'bennin's' on top of the line.

As a security measure there should then be a lashing across the top of the heap to keep the line in the basket till required.

Bait for such a line is usually herring cut in halves or maybe in three if the herring are scarce.

The actual process of baiting could also be described as hooking the bait. If you are baiting a 'head-half' the hook must go in through the back of the head and out through the back of the neck; a tail-half requires the hook in and out through the bone so that the bait will stay on the hook. See?

Now, let's get a start to shoot the lines. The basket is placed close to the bulwark with the 'bare' rim toward the sea and facing somewhat aft.

Two of you will be seated on fishboxes with a box of cut bait between you, and as the ship steams ahead and the line goes zipping over the side you'll take it in turn to bait and throw the hooks clear of the line.

Immediately on the aft side of you a man will be 'running the back', checking that the line runs clear and in one hand he'll have a razor-sharp knife in case of accidents.

The bottom end of the line is 'bent' (never 'tied') to the top end of the next line so that the basket when empty can be whisked away and a full basket set in its place without a moment's slacking of the pace.

If you want a fag, someone else will have to give you a lighted one, because you 'canna tak' yer e'e aff yer wark'!

You must not dither yet you must not be rash and on no account must you let a hook drop into the basket among the line. That would be a disaster. Great-line hooks are lethal and must be handled with care.

Basket after basket, mile after mile of line, several thousand hooks, in conditions which are always bitterly cold and often very wet indeed; then ye'll ken fit caal is!

Well now, let's get back to Loch Glendhu where the Turk has anchored a few nets as close to the shore as it was safe to go with a drifter. Nets on anchors? Aye, surely! There's nae room to drift!

The supper table has been cleared and the lads are having a smoke when the Turk makes a dramatic announcement, 'Jeemsie, my loon, I think I've gotten a flech!'

Nae again, skipper? Flechs seems t' like you! Far is she this time, back or front?

'Verra near atween my shooder blades. At least that's far she is eyenoo!'

'Fine!' says Jeemsie, 'That's jist fine! There's nae near so mony lurks an fauls on yer back as there is on yer belly so we'll ha'e a better chance o' catchin' her! Ye mind the job we had catchin' the last een 'cos she wis hidin' among the caddis (fluff) in yer belly-button! Lat's ha'e the tail o' yer linner, skip!'

Behold now, the Turk, face down on the cabin table beneath the only light available, the white glare from the naked flame of the acetylene gas jet.

And behold his gallant crew, completely engrossed as they watch Jeemsie rowin' up the mannies linner, canny, canny . . . !

'Better nor the picters, this!' says Duncan.

'Better nor readin' the labels on the jam-jars!' says Lugs, the fireman.

'Gie's a bittie slack, skipper! I canna work athoot slack!' says Jeemsie.

The tension was terrific for a while, till Jeemsie made a lightning pounce before bolting up the trap with his prey.

'I've catched the brute skipper! I'll throw her ower the side! Jist 'ee listen for the splash 'cos she's near as big's a labster!'

Amid the laughter which followed the Turk rearranged his clothing. 'An affa loon that,' says he. 'But he's a great han' among the flechs. I'm richt gled it wis a flech an' nae a bog. Fin I wis in the Navy we wis affa sair bothered wi' bogs!'

'I didna ken there wis bogs at Trafalgar,' says Duncan. 'I thocht that wis on the open sea!'

'I'm nae spikkin' aboot weet grun', ye gowk, I mean yon beasties that sooks yer bleed fin ye're sleepin'! The Navy ships wis crawlin' wi' them but ye see they were a' English boats. If we had a Scotch navy we wid flee the Lion Rompin' an' there widna be a bog t' be seen!'

'Wid they be feart at the lion?' says Duncan.

'Lach if ye like, my freen,' says the Turk. 'But if ye get bogs in the ship ye'll ken a' aboot it. They like t' bide in the seams atween the planks an' they breed at twa thoosan' per cent.

'I've seen some lads gaun along the seams wi' reid-het pokers an' you could hear the beasties crackin' like spunks! They sook bleed until they burst an' syne the stink wid scumfish ye! They're nae gweed company!'

'Fan are we lookin'-on skipper?' says Dumplin's in a hurry.

'The twalt 'oor!' says the Turk. 'Ye'd better sleep fast!'

On the stroke of midnight the watchman called the sleeping crew by rattling a mug with a spoon and saying sweetly 'Haway now, Haway! Rise an' shine!' His shipmates obeyed immediately and sat down to enjoy their scalding hot tea.

But, alas, the poor Turk was in a parlous state. He sat beside his bunk in fear and trembling, great beads of sweat on his brow.

'Fit's adee, skipper? Are ye nae-weel?' cried Jeemsie.

'If that wis a', I wid be fine, my loon, but I'm feart that the worst has come hinmaist! There's been something aitin' me a' nicht till my back's fair raw an' it canna be onything but bogs! Will ye ha'e a look, Jeemsie?'

'Nae fears!' says the loon. 'A flech's jist a flech but I'm for naething t' dee wi' bogs!'

'C'mon skip! Doon the stoke-hole wi' me an' we'll ha'e a look!' says Duncan, and the Turk obeyed meekly.

To a man the crew followed, each and every one with an uneasy itchy feeling atween his shooder blades. From various vantage points they watched in fascination as Duncan seized the skipper's linner an' yarkit it up ower his heid.

'Dalmichty! I nivver saw the likes o' this afore, skipper. There's great teethmarks a' ower yer back! Dis bogs ha'e teeth?'

'Nae as far as I ken, Duncan!'

'That's fit I thocht, skipper. An' ye'd better stop makkin' sic a soun', 'cos it's time ye wis learnin' that a man o' your wecht shouldna' sleep on his ain false teeth!'

KIRKYARD RAIN

I'm thinking back on Davy –
　He'd aye his ain luck!
Wi' canny speed he'd forge aheid
　Tho' ither folk were stuck.
When better men than Davy
　Could get nae fish ava
The cod wid steer for Davy's gear
　An' gie themsel's awa'.

But lat's be fair to Davy –
　It wisna' Davy's blame
That tempest wild lay meek an' mild
　Till Davy had won hame.
An' tho' ye'll 'gree that Davy
　Had better luck than maist,
Ye'd surely say this very day,
　'We kent it couldna laist!'

Weel! here to bury Davy
　There's mair than half the fleet,
A teemin' sky – still Davy's dry
　But we're a' dreepin' weet!

LEEBIE

I couldna spell, I couldna coont past twinty,
Nor could I read unless the words were sma',
I couldna name the highest hill in England,
For maps were things for hingin' on the wa',
I couldna mind a date nor place a battle,
And so I was 'The girl who was no use
For any earthly purpose whatsoever!'
So said yon primpit craitur, young Miss Bruce.

The years ha'e flown, the aul'er aye the faster,
The kings and queens, the battles are forgot,
I've kent this fyle the highest hill in England,
Tho' learnin'-wise I hinna gained a lot.
But I've my man an' fower bonny bairnies,
A happy hame far some folk has a Hoose;
An' sometimes, when I think hoo I've been guided,
I greet for yon peer craitur, aul' Miss Bruce.

WHERE THERE'S LIFE

'Fit like are 'ee the day?' says I.
Til a freen' I've kent since days gone by.

'Weel noo!' says he an' he draws his breath,
'I've been this fyle at the door o' death!
Ye'll mind last 'ear I took the flu?
Weel, I'm only gettin' the back o't noo,
But it's teen a gey sair pick, ye'll see,
For I'm lantered noo wi' a cockle 'e'e.
There's inflammation in my jints,
So I canna boo doon to tie my pints,
An' if I try't my bubbly nose,
Begins to skite like a gairden hose,
An' afore I get pooer to gie't a dicht,
It jist rins dry an' it bungs up ticht.
Syne that affects my peer aul' heid,
An' it lies on my shooders like a lump o' leed,
So ye'll see my loon (an he stoppit for breath),
Jist fit it's like at the door o' death!
I'm bothered fyles wi' my water tee,
An' its twenty times a day, ye see,
It's nae neen handy tho' it's nae ower sair,
But ye ken oor bathroom's up the stair.
My bowels hisna meeved for a fyle,
So I doot it's back to the castor ile,
An' that itsel's nae fine, ye ken,
For ye canna get peace for a meenit on en'.
Like the atom boom it works on the dot,
So I'm up the stairs like a mountain goat!
Ye speir at me "Fit like?" That's feel!
Ye can surely see that I'm nae neen weel'

'There's nae muckle wrang wi' yer sicht!' says I.
As he eyed a deem that wis passin' by.

THE SKIPPER'S WIFE

Jock, neist door, has a score o' cran,
    But yer father hisna neen.
They say there's a hantle o' herrin' tee,
    So far can the gowk ha'e been?
He'll seen be hame wi's foul black face,
    An' he'll look for mait, 'at's mair.
An' he'll fidge an' pech an' he'll grunt an' blaw
    Like a bear fin its belly's sair,
He'll ha'e to be deein' wi' pottet heid
    Tho' its nae jist ower sair jeeled.
'Anither tattie or twa,' did ye say?
    'Na, we'll just chap the thing 'at's peeled;'
It's a gey sair fecht, an' it's true aneuch
    The wordle's ill-pairtit for some o's;
It's time he wis gettin' a shottie noo
    Or it's gweed kens fit'll come o's.

Jock, neist door, has a cran or twa,
    But yer father's a hunner and twinty!
Hing in noo quine! Rin for fillet steak,
    An' be sure m'dear ye get plinty,
An' ye'll sort it richt wi' a fine fresh egg
    An' a bonny hame-made chip;
An' ye'd better cry-tee for a curran' dad
    For he disna get that in the ship.
Is there plinty o' watter het noo quine?
    He'll be yirdit wi' scales an' saut.
If he starts t' sing like the Rattra' horn,
    Jist dinna say it's a faut.
He's a richt smairt man yer father, quine,
    There's fyowe on the coast to beat 'im,
I think I'll pit on my Sunday hat
    An' ging doon on the pier to meet 'im.

CRAIGEWAN

Pace-aiggs bricht on the yalla san'
   In the pale clear sun o' Spring.
Young heids bent in a kysie search
   'Mong the rocks far limpets cling.
Lang fine days wi' their happy ploys,
   An' bare feet rinnin' free;
The lilt o' win' throu' wavin' girss,
   An' the strong clear call o' the sea.

Lad-'n-lass traivlin' airm-in-airm.
   Owre the bents on a simmer's nicht,
Sweir t'ging hame, like a' their kind,
   Tho' the sun's lang oot o' sicht.
The cry o' a whaup at the watter-mou',
   An' the smell o' the tangle-bree;
The whisper o' win' throu' quiverin' girss,
   An' the low saft sang o' the sea.

Oot-win, caul wi' the threat o' rain,
   Or it micht be wi' grey sea fog.
An' fa's on the bare grey bents the day
   But an aul' grey man wi's dog.
Traivlin' the aul' paths, hearin' soun's
   O' the days that eesed t'be
In the sough o' win' throu' shiverin' girss,
   An' the dreary dirge o' the sea.

YE WIDNA BE SELLT!
(For a Special Day)

Were I a poet, lass o' mine,
   I'd snare the crescent moon
An' set it in a bonny line
   To rhyme wi' rose in June;
The proper bard pits flooers an' birds
   In sangs o' love, that's true,
But lass, I dinna ha'e the words
   To say sic things to you!

Were I to whisper 'Precious heart'!
   Ye'd think I wisna weel!
Or, did I mention Cupid's dart,
   Ye'd say 'Ye great aul' feel'!
A fancy card I micht ha'e bocht –
   'Twid been an easier plan,
But lass, ye're worth a sweeter thocht
   Than verse that's second-han'.

For mony a year, for mony a mile
   We've sodjered on thegither;
Could words that made oor bairnies smile
   Nae still delight their mither?
Then harken close my sonsie lass –
   Fit better could I tell ye?
'Tho' moons an' Junes awa' may pass
   Ye ken I widna sell ye!'

THE CHOICE

Were I but young an' feel again –
   An' that can hardly be,
I'd like to mak' a change or twa;
   I widna seek the sea.
Could I but pick an' chyse again
   I'd tramp anither road,
An' keep my fit weel plantit
   On the firm dry sod.

Could I but pick an' chyse again,
   I'd like a wiser heid,
Then in the ups an' doons o' life
   I micht come mair speed;
But were I at the start again
   An' tellt ae choice was mine,
It's land or sea I'd taikle –
   Wi' the same aul' quine.

A TIME TO GET

They tell me, loon ye've left the school;
   Ye'd like to try the sea.
Your mither's sent ye doon the road
   To seek advice fae me?
She micht a' socht some better chiel
   To keep her loonie richt
But sit ye doon; I'll dee my best
   To shed a bittie licht
On paths that dark afore ye lie
   If fishin' be your aim
Syne if some day ye rue the start
   Ye'll ha'e yersel' to blame.

Ye'll lowse the rope, a cocky chiel,
   Gran' notions in your heid.
Afore ye're oot o' sicht o' lan'
   Ye'll wish that ye wis deid,
For sickness disna pick an' chyse;
   It lays the mighty low.
Ye'll lie an' shiver on the deck
   Nae fit to ging below.
'If only she wid bide at peace!'
   But that can nivver be
Ye've left the steady lan' astarn
   An' noo ye're on the sea.

But that'll wear awa' come time;
   Ye'll learn to keep your feet.
Ye'll walk the deck as deil-may-care
   As if it were the street.
Till some coorse day she'll tak' a lump
   An' then ye'll get a scare!
Ye'll sweel aboot the scuppers
   An' ye'll learn the lesson there
That nae sometimes, but a' the time
   Ye need a wary e'e.
Ye've left the steady lan' astarn
   An' noo ye're on the sea.

A growin' loon, a workin' loon
    Ye'll aye cry oot for mait,
An' then ye'll learn the secret knack
    O' keepin't in your plate.
The table's showdin' up an' doon,
    It's reelin' back an' fore
An' tattie soup tak's queer-like tigs
    It nivver took ashore.
High broadside motion nivver moved
    Your mither's kitchen fleer –
But that was in the steady world
    Ye've left upon the pier.

Ye'll learn to tyauve along wi' men,
    Ye'll work the clock aroon'.
Ye'll rise afore the summer sun,
    Ye'll see him beddit doon.
Come winter an' ye'll get a taste
    O' lang nichts black wi' sleet.
The bitter, bitin' cruel caul
    Wid gar a buddy greet.
The time'll come ye'd sell your sowl
    For twa sweet 'oors o' sleep.
The lowsin' times for folk ashore
    Are eeseless on the deep.

As time wears on ye'll see the sichts
    Ye'd nivver see on lan'.
There's beauty in the wilderness
    An' wisdom in the plan
O' calm an' storm, o' flood an' ebb;
    For a'thing there's a reason.
The ocean, like the fruitful earth,
    Has everything in season.
'A time to plant and a time to reap'
    Suits fairmin' to the letter;
'A time to get and a time to lose'
    Would fit the fishin' better.

A year or twa, my bonny loon,
    An' then ye'll be a man,
Weel worth a place in ony crew,
    An' fit to turn your han'
To ony job your trade requires
    Wi' needle or wi' knife;
As gweed, ye'll think, as plenty that's
    Been at it a' their life.
In time o' want – an' come it will,
    Ye'll think the skipper's feel;
Ye'd mak' a better job yersel'
    Could 'ee but get the wheel.

Gin 'ee be spared an' weel, my loon
    Ye'll get the chance ana'.
In your domain ye'll be the king –
    Ye'll ha'e the thocht o't a!
Is't north or sooth, is't aff or on?
    Is't line or drift or seine?
Ye'll hum an' haw an' claw your pow
    But answer maun be gi'en.
An' gin ye're aftener richt than wrang
    Ye'll be a lucky man,
But richt or wrang aye keep in mind
    Ye've men's lives in your han'.

Ye ken yersel' sun moon an' star
    Are seldom seen thegither.
An' so it is wi' shots o' fish,
    Gweed prices, bonny wither.
There's aye a something wantin' loon,
    Ye'll seldom get the three,
An' mony a time ye'll tell yersel'
    That een o' them wid dee.
'A time to plant and a time to reap'
    Suits fairmin' to the letter
'A time to get and a time to lose'
    Would fit the fishin' better.

Ye're young an' strong, ye're quick an' keen
  Nae doot ye'll tak' your share
I dinna think ye'll be a feel
  That wither disna scare.
'Gainst wind and wave, the biggest boat's
  A verra sma' defence.
A lot that looks like iron nerves
  Is just the want o' sense.
But common sense wi' patience mixed
  Will help ye guide the wheel.
I think, come time ye'll learn them baith,
  Gweed-nicht. I wish ye weel.

THE INCOMER

Sandy Todd was the biggest chiel
  That ivver trod this earth'
He was come o' a rovin' tinkie tribe
  Fae the foreign side o' Perth.
He was broad in the beam like a garage door,
  An' I'm sure he was nine-foot three
The day he came North for a job at the ile
  An' to bide next door to me.

Sandy Todd was the strongest man
  I'd ever seen in my life
An' the things he could dee wi's great muckle han's
  Fair mesmerised the wife.
He could fire a steen as far as the meen,
  He could haaver a tree in twa,
An' to cairry coal a ton at a time
  Was jist nae bother ava.
He could lift a fathom o' railway line
  An' bend it ower his knee;
Noo the wife thinks she was thrown awa'
  When she mairried a dreep like me.

Sandy Todd was the finest cook
  That ever steered a pot:
He could taikle a ten course jamboree
  An' master-mind the lot.
His beef-steak pies won a special prize
  This year at the Turra Show,
When a certain firm sent a spy to steal
  The secrets o' his dough.
But he widna stoop to tattie soup
  Or stovers or potted heid,
For that was grub ye could get in a pub
  Wi' folk o' a lesser breed
His damson tart was a work of art
  That thousands came to see;
Noo the wife thinks she's been thrown awa'
  On an eesless lump like me.

Sandy Todd was the smairtest chiel
 That ever yet drew breath;
He could ficher wi' ony mortal thing
 Fae marzipan to claith.
He could sort a slate, or hing a gate,
 Or alter a slidin' door.
He carved a statue o' Robbie Burns
 Fae wid washen up on the shore.
There wisna a job in a' this earth
 That Sandy couldna dee;
Noo the wife thinks she's been thrown awa'
 On a warriedrag like me.

Sandy Todd was the best kent chiel
 This toon has ever seen;
He was fine acquaint wi' the Prince o' Wales,
 An' Liz was his name for the Queen.
He expressed the hope he would meet the Pope
 Again, when he went to Rome,
An' he tellt me his country residence
 Was as big as the Parish Home.
He collieshangied wi' Arab sheiks
 An' ithers o' high degree;
Noo the wife jist disna ken fit wye
 She bides wi' the likes o' me.

But there's been a change this day or twa;
 A change, I think, for the better.
I'm expectin' the bobbies doon the nicht
 Wi' a special kind o' letter.
For noo it's me that's the smairtest chiel
 That ever yet was born;
I stuck a knife in Sandy Todd
 An' he's buryin' the morn.

GALE WARNING

Hear the oft repeated tale –
 'Fresh-to-strong soon reaching gale,
Wintry showers of sleet and hail
 Spreading from the west.'
Ragged clouds of sombre grey,
 Mourners of the dying day,
Ride the winds that tear the spray
 From each snarling crest.

Darkness falls, the wild sky clears,
 Crystal bright each star appears,
While the Merry Dancer's spears
 Cleave the bitter north.
Now the banshee sea-wind raves
 O'er her host of maddened slaves;
She, the mistress of the waves,
 Drives her minions forth.

See, from out the eerie night,
 Roaring demons plumed in white
Hurl their weight with cruel spite,
 O'er the weather rail,
Seeking in their wrath to deal
 Blows that make our stout bark reel,
Tortured sore from truck to keel,
 'Neath their awful flail.

While the slow hours onward creep,
 Weary eyes their vigil keep.
Aching limbs that long for sleep,
 Peace nor respite find.
Hearts that fear can seldom move
 Hope, with breaking day, to prove –
'Even tho' the earth remove
 Providence is kind.'

NOT TO THE SWIFT

Jock an' Daavit played thegither
  On the rocky Buchan braes;
Focht an' greed wi' een anither
  A' their happy childhood days.
Shared their humble bits o' treasures
  Chance aboot, for friendship's sake;
Shared their simple hamely pleasures,
  Pleased to see an antrin maik.

Schooldays cam' wi' books an' learnin';
  Readin', spellin', three times three,
Jock an' Daavit chafin', yearnin'
  Fae their prison to be free.
Scoltit for their careless writin',
  Keepit in for bein' late;
Spent the weary time o' wytin'
  Drawin' shippies on a slate.

Schooldays deen, they left thegither;
  Sang like linties to be free,
Left ae prison for anither,
  Noo their jiler wis the sea.
'Work a' nicht, my willin' nippers!
  Sleep the time o' steamin' aff,
Dream o' days when you'll be skippers;
  Royal dreams on beds o' caff!'

O the joy o' distant places,
  Ports they'd nivver seen afore.
Like the desert's green oasis
  Sweet the antrin nicht ashore.
Yarmouth lichts shone clearer, rarer,
  Wi' the glamour o' the name,
And the stranger lass seemed fairer
  Than the fisher quine at hame.

Lily waters, ragglish wither,
  Wintry blast or summer haze,
Jock and Daavit wrocht thegither
  Shipmates, a' their decky days.
Till the path they trod divided
  Into twa, as paths aye will,
An' maturer years decided
  Each should clim' his ain hill.

Pairted? Aye, but nivver striven;
  Skippers wi' a boat apiece.
Jock was pleased to get a livin';
  Daavit socht the golden fleece
Where the distant fields loomed greener
  Wi' the glamour o' the name.
Jock, peer, canny sowl wid seener
  Puddle oot an' in at hame.

Nivver aff the sea was Daavit,
  Gross the aim an' fame the goad,
Sleepin' wore his boots an' graavit,
  Sabbath days were in his road.
Jock could steal an' 'oor for leisure
  On the sunny bowlin'-green.
Or to walk in sweetest pleasure
  Up the waterside wi' Jean.

On the scroll o' fishin' glory
  Daavit's name's abeen them a'.
Seldom in the 'hale lang story
  Will ye hear o' Jock ava.
Thus 'twid seem that a' thegither
  Daavit cam' the better speed.
Yet this ae thing gars me swither –
  Jock's aye livin', Daavit's deid.

THE DUNDERHEID

Oh, he was thick! Man, he couldna coont
The product o' three times three,
But that was a gift that the Lord had kept
For his favoured sons like me.
He sat at the fitt o' the snicherin' class
Wi' his battered bag at his feet,
An' the dytit wye that he thocht an' spoke
Wid ha'e gart an angel greet

Oh boys, he was thick!

Oh, he was thick! Man, he coudna tell
A snatchie o' verse fae prose,
But that was a gift that the Lord had kept
For those an' such as those.
He sat at the fitt o' the snicherin' class
An' man, ye wid scarce believe
That to clean his slate he spat in its face
Syne gied it a rub wi' his sleeve.

Oh boys, he was thick!

Oh, he was thick! Man, he couldna see
That the verb was the predicate,
But that was a gift that the Lord had kept
Fae the loon that was short o' mait.
He sat at the fitt o' the snicherin' class
In his orra'like sheen an hose,
An' he seemed to think that the back o' his han'
Was for dichtin' his bubbly nose.

Oh boys, he was thick!

I've jist been readin' the daily news
An' there, in the centre spot,
He's sellt some ships to finance a Hame
For bairns that the world forgot.
He's miles aheid o' the snicherin' class
An' I've learned wi' shame on my face,
That it's nae for me nor my class to decide
The gift, nor the time, nor the place.

Oh Lord, I've been thick!

HAME COMFORT

A wife that I ken has a bonny Room
    Wi' a fleer like polished glaiss,
An' the sun peepin' in thro' the spotless screens,
    Gets blin't wi' the bleeze o' braiss.

There's this and there's that o' the latest style,
    An' the dearest o' fancy suites;
An' could ye but tramp on the basses there,
    I'm sure ye wid sink to the queets.

There's nivver a mark o' stue in the place,
    For it's ower weel cleaned an' dichtit.
An' the grate! Aswarn it wid heat a kirk.
    If the fire wis iver lichtit.

Her man has a seat that's as hard's a steen
    In the barfit kitchen en'.
He kens there's a far better cheer in the Room,
    But he kens he daurna ging ben.

So he sits in the draucht wi' a dreep at 'is nose,
    An' a hackin' hoast at 'is breist,
An' he growls as he glowers at the skimpit fire –
    'It's a fittit carpet neist!'

But he shouldna girn, for he ocht to ken,
    If he'd ony sense in his heid,
That he'll get a chance o' the Room some day
    Fin he's caul' an' stiff an' deid.

THE WIN' IN 'IS FACE

Some folk get the win' in their face
  A' their mortal days,
Fine div they ken the desert place
  Wi' its dreich an' craggy braes.
Theirs is the world o' trauchlin' thro';
  Theirs is a dour grey sky.
For the sunny spell an' the gentle dew
  Seem aye to pass them by.

Some folk get the win' at their backs;
  Theirs is a lichtsome birn,
Wi' nivver a flaw in the fine-spun flax
  They draw fae the birlin' pirn.
Theirs is the world o' fill-an'-fess-ben,
  Theirs is a bricht blue sky,
For the caul' roch shooer that weets ither men
  Seems aye to leave them dry.

Some can smile in their weary lot
  Altho' the fecht be sair;
Some ha'e aye the greet in their throat
  Tho' they've neither cark nor care.
Keep 'ee the chiel fae the sheltered place
  Wi's hert as caul' as a steen,
I'll tak' the lad wi' the win' in 'is face
  An' I'll ha'e a better freen.

Biggest lee you are ever likely to hear

'A'body's a lot better aff noo, but they're nae near so happy an' contintit as they eesed t' be!'

This is an expression you'll hear every day and usually it is accompanied by a lugubrious shake of the head. By their very nature the words can only be used by an ageing generation and in fact they form the biggest lee you are ever likely to hear!

Nae doot ye'll be sayin' – 'We aye kent he wis feel, but he's due for the asylum noo!' But that would be a fatal mistake. Listen!

It was in the early thirties and it was to be my last year at school. But altho' I little knew it, my education simply had not begun!

In the middle of December Cousin Jim 'wis teen awa' t' Aiberdeen wi' pendix' and his mother, worried about her son's health and also worried at the prospects of Jim 'lossin' his message-boy jobbie' came round to see if I could possibly get off school to keep his jobbie open.

Special dispensation was granted and I joyfully assumed the role of message-boy with John M. Thomson (Grocer) in the Longate in Peterhead. At that time the Longate was one unbroken line of all kinds of shops (on both sides) and the maze of lanes and closes which ran from the street towards the harbour gave access to a welter of dingy slums and hovels populated by an unbelievable number of people.

Coal-heavers, stevedores, coopers and kipperers with a scattering of fisher folk were crowded together in appalling conditions and they were all afflicted with one common disease, namely poverty. Their bairns would come to the shop just before it closed at 8 p.m., as all shops did in those days, asking for 'chippit aipples' or 'broken biscuits' which were of course sold at reduced prices, and 'on tick' forbye!

Keepin' the chippit aipples aside was part of my job along wi' wyin' oot half-steens o' tatties an' fillin' jars wi' seerip. The customer would bring an empty jam-jar when she wanted seerip 'cos athoot an empty, the seerip wis a maik dearer!

Did iver ye try fillin' jars wi' seerip oot o' a barrel? Boys, that would further your education! It fairly furthered mine! Ae richt caul frosty mornin', I was at this job in the back shop. The seerip wis stiff wi' caul an' it wisna ower willin' t' come oot o' the barrel.

It wis tricklin' into the jar in slow, lazy fauls when the boss shouted for me to wye tatties, so I jumped to it! But oh, the love o' Dod Vricht, I forgot to shut the cockie!

It wis twa 'oors afore I got back an' boys ye nivver saw sic a sotter; the 'hale back shop wis awash wi' seerip, a clorty, sticky sea wi' islands here an' there. The peer cat wis marooned richt in the middle, on an orange-box reef!

I didna expect the lifeboat wid come for a cat so I just gid in ower the boot-heids an' saved the craitur. I didna get a medal! I learned that day that seerip's nae gweed t' shift wi' a shovel! Specially if it's mixed wi' paper an' bitties o' cork! Educational? Aye, surely!

Hogmanay came roon' an' I wis nivver aff my bike gaun' wi' orders. Ten bob the week plus tips; a proper fortin! I often got a penny fae wifies that could ill spare the tip but nivver a copper did I get at the gran' hooses in the select part o' the toon!

At midnicht on Hogmanay I was sent to Jimmy Reid's to get a horse an' cairt to get the orders delivered and I lowsed at half past two on New Year's mornin'! And I really enjoyed it!

Noo, listen again! In those days a 'hale bourachie o' folk had their hames on the 'Queenie', ower the brig fae the toon. The Queenie is actually the water you have to cross to get to Keith Inch which was once an island, so anyone 'Gaun ower the Queenie' was doing exactly that, but somehow the name got transposed to the actual island itself whose inhabitants were known as Queenie Arabs.

The mixture as before – fisher folk and tradesmen, decent hard-workin' folk sair afflicted wi' poverty.

Well, here was I on the Queenie, gropin' my wye up a black, dark close, then up a darker steen stair to the outside door o' the hoose. It wis darker than yer oxter pooch inside the door so it wis a case o' feelin' my road up a widden stair which my feet tellt me wis completely bare and badly worn.

The door at the stair-heid had nae knob, jist a sneck, and my sharp rap on its face brocht the cry 'Come in, my loon!' As seen as I opened the door a great blast o' rick came doon the lum an' the gas licht started to blink. Oh boys, what a place to bide!

I put the basket on a chair then began to transfer its contents to the table, closely watched by three bairns who sat on a low stool by the fire. Suddenly they jumped to their feet and careered round the table like Red Indians, clappin' their hands and chantin' 'Seerip, seerip, seerip!'

'Fit on earth's adee wi' the bairns?' says I.

'Ye can surely see that' says the mither, 'Seerip's a special treat for Hogmanay! They're excited wytin for their Da t' come hame fae the trawlin' the nicht.'

So there were five in the one attic! And a jar o' syrup was a special treat!

Now listen again! If ye can equate such conditions wi' happiness an' contintment, I'll gi'e ye a fiver!

An' should ye try to pass this off as an isolated incident ye'd be clean wrang.

I was message boy wi' John M. Thomson an' I ken different!

The lost tribe of the Auchies

There is no such thing as 'the fisher tongue', simply because there are as many variations in the fisher tongue as there are fisher communities on the coast.

It is quite possible for a keen ear to pinpoint the very village of a fisherbody's origin by noting the inflections and subtle nuances of the speaker's voice.

Boddam is not very far from Peterhead but the difference in their speech is really quite obvious. Buchanhaven, in my youth, was a fisher community completely separate from Peterhead and one could easily recognise a 'Buchaner' by his accent.

Now that Buchanhaven has been for many years engulfed in the big town, the difference in accent has been largely smoothed out, but this applies only to the younger generation. Their elders are quite easily spotted.

Even in the big town itself the Doric has been grossly diluted with excessive doses of John Wayne and the like. When I hear youngsters say 'It's richt caul, is it?' my ear is deeply offended because such a statement is not merely a grammatical error – it is an abomination.

It would appear that this dilution of the Doric is more or less unavoidable but it is nonetheless regrettable.

Still, one must be thankful that there are still such terms as skurry, myaave and pule, all of them names for the common gull and each one a definite pointer to the native locality of the user. The watering down of local dialects is common along the whole coastline and I'm afraid it is especially evident in the village of Auch (Avoch).

When I was a lad many 'Auchies' came to Peterhead to find berths in the herring drifters. Indeed many of them married local quines and settled down in the Blue Toon.

On a Sunday morning there would be several pews of Auchies in the Conger Kirk, each one in his navy blue ganjie and black silk 'muffler'.

Their speech was almost incomprehensible and indeed to meet an 'Auchie' with a habber was a severe test of endurance. Their term for ham and egg was ''am an' heygg' and when they meant 'sma' herrin' ' they said 'smaalairing'.

The Auchies were mostly dark-haired and of medium build. They were and still are very hard-working men of a rather quiet disposition. I am not really competent to trace their origins, but I have a suspicion that they are a race apart.

With surnames like Patience and Jack how could they be anything else?

I have heard them described as the Lost Tribe of Israel and I have also heard a whisper that they are descended from a remnant of Cromwell's army which ventured too far north and got themselves surrounded by hordes of war-like Hielanmen.

I think the latter conjecture would be more likely especially if the term 'Hielanmen' were deleted and 'Hielan Deems' put in its place.

Be this as it may, the Auchies are decent folk and if I consider their speech as comical, no doubt they laugh themselves silly at my uncouth Buchan vernacular.

Avoch is a lovely village in a lovely setting. It stands on the north shore of the Inverness Firth. (Not the Moray Firth, you silly! Where's your geography?)

To enter the Inverness Firth you must leave the Moray Firth and take the narrow channel between Fort George and the Chanonry. When you have negotiated this channel you are in the Inverness Firth and away to starboard you'll see Auch with its whitewashed houses.

Away in the distance ahead you'll see Inverness and the new Kessock Bridge and should you pass under that lofty span you'll be in the Beauly Firth. See?

The two Firths form a huge, land-locked expanse of calm water which for many years was the scene for a fruitful winter herring fishing. Herring? Aye! The 'smaalairing'!

They were bigger than sprats but much smaller than normal herrings, and there were times when the shoals were very thick indeed.

Fancy shooting a fleet of nets away up in the Beauly Firth at high-water so that you could drift with the ebb through the narrows at the Kessock Ferry! Or drifting from Kilmuir across Munlochy Bay then down past Avoch!

I have heard that the ferryman at Kessock used to set a net at the slipway and when he got a 'good marking' the Auchies got their nets aboard and the season proper would commence.

The nets used for catching the 'garvies' (as the small herrings were often called) were of course narrow in the mesh, very shallow to suit the shallow waters and made of white cotton. They were never barked or tanned, but were steeped regularly in a boiling solution of alum.

The traditional method of weighting the nets was to get stones from the beach – special stones in that they had strong tufts of brown seaweed sprouting from them. By hitching the seaweed to the bottom rope of the nets you could get ballast which would scuff along the seabed without chafing any tows. A proper Stone Age practice!

When the fleet grew larger, such stones were as scarce as hen's teeth and a substitute had to be found.

At last some clever youth came up with the idea of using old metal floats from seine nets. These floats had a metal lug on them and if you punctured the metal sphere so that it could be filled with cement you had a perfect sinker.

This was the death knell for the stone weights!

Some of the boaties which prosecuted this particular fishing were not very big at all. Indeed some of them were 'scaphs' or 'scaffies' which were as old as the hills, having been built originally for sails. These scaffies were only 25-30 feet in length, but most of the fleet was composed of first-class modern craft, 1950s style. Fifty-footers or a bittie bigger.

When the Peterhead inshore fleet decided to horn in on this fine canny fishing, it was proper pandemonium. There were boats and nets all over the place and we discovered that it wasn't nearly so canny as we had expected.

It was a case of shoot and haul the whole night through because in these restricted waters with their strong tides you could not possibly let her lie all night. On occasion it reminded me of the Dodgems at the shows.

I shall never forget one night in particular. We had drifted down from the Longman with the ebb but before we finished hauling the tide had carried us so far that we were away to seaward of the Chanonry lighthouse. For that haul we had twelve crans so I thought we would steam up the Firth again and repeat the operation.

The narrow channel was choc-a-bloc with boats and nets so the only practical way was to nip past on the east side of the melee.

Clever me, until the boat came to a sudden halt! We were well and truly stuck on the sewage pipe which runs down the beach from Fort George.

This pipe is on concrete supports and its top surface would be at least five feet off the bottom. I was black affronted for a while until one of the Auch skippers said very kindly: 'Was that your first time on the pipe, Peter? It winna be your last! It happens so often that we think nothing of it!'

Comfort indeed!

I think the Inverness Firth must be one of the coldest spots in the country. There is a great deal of fresh water around and that is always colder than salt water.

It was quite common to see great sheets of ice coming down from the River Ness and I have seen herrings only a few minutes out of the water being snapped like twigs – so severe was the frost. I had never believed this possible until I tried it myself.

To work in such conditions is no picnic, especially when one is suffering from lack of sleep.

They say that 'Ilka cock craws on his ain midden heid'!

Local knowledge is a tremendous asset but it cannot be gained overnight. It may take years to acquire this precious commodity, but to spend years at the 'smaalairing'? Brrrr! Nothing doing!

'Hale eggs from the Pearl King!

It was a bitterly cold day with a thin layer of fresh snow when my Deydie (grandad) and I took the bus to go 'up the country'.

It was 1925 and I was a very small boy whom Deydie addressed as 'littlin' or 'boakie' as his humour dictated. Among all the host of Deydie's grandchildren I was his favourite, his right-hand man, his special envoy, his bosom friend, and many's the time I accompanied him on his rural wanderings.

Sometimes we would go to Neebra (Newburgh) to see about mussel bait; sometimes we would 'tak' a bittie fish' to yon mannie at the Moss o' Rora. We kent a Longside mannie that made a wooden chain oot o' ae bit o' timmer and we kent a mannie in Crichie who had 'lost the wife' since he last had seen us.

Only the tone of Deydie's voice as he said 'Eh man! Eh, man!' prevented me from offering to go and look for her. I was as young as that!

Well now, this particular day we were on a special mission; in fact we were on two missions rolled into one. The first was to obtain two horse tails, 'a black een an' a fite een'! The best place for such a prize was of course a farm for in those days tractors were as yet unknown.

We would take the tails home where they would be thoroughly washed and combed, then Deydie would make horse-hair 'tippins' for his haddock lines.

I would give him seven hairs from a tail; he would deftly knot the seven ends into one before drawing the hairs across a leather pad strapped to his leg above the knee while at the same time he rolled the hairs together with his left hand. Then he would finish the job with another neat knot. The end result was a beautiful glossy string of amazing lightness and strength, about eighteen inches long, and onto this 'tippin' he would 'beat' (lash) the hook.

The workmanship was superb and the patience incredible. My job entailed keeping an eye on the tatties which were roasting on the bink (hob) of the grate. Left-overs from dinner time when they had been boiled in their jackets, they were very good indeed. Champions or Buchan Beauties they were. What was radio? What was TV? Ye must be clean daft!

Our second errand was to find some 'speyngie' or 'spaingie'.

Note that the end of that word is pronounced in the same way as 'springy' or 'thingie' and it means the cane from which baskets are made. Deydie had heard that speyngie was to be obtained at a certain farm and since he was an ardent basket maker he was keen to acquire some raw materials. A very versatile mannie was Deydie.

So we left the bus at the first roadie past the Prison and made our way on foot through the snow. When we had covered about half a mile we met a great muckle deem who ventured to remark that it was 'Helluva caul'!

'Prodeegious caul!' says Deydie, who didna use bad words. Some twenty paces further on he suddenly stopped and turned to survey the receding female, and dashit if she didn't do exactly the same.

So there the two of them stood glowering speechless at each other. Young as I was I was highly amused.

Deydie was the first to give in so we resumed our way with him muttering 'My govies, littlin', did ye ivver see legs like yon?'

After an interminable walk we arrived at our destination, the farm named Wellbank. 'Noo!' says Deydie 'This is far the Pearl King bides an' his name's Mister Birnie! See that ye behave yersel'!' I was glad to get inside to the warmth of the kitchen fire.

The Pearl King, as he was universally known, had made a heap o' siller oot East by employing natives to dive for pearls. Naked except for a loin cloth, the divers fastened a big stone to their ankles before plunging overboard from the boat. The purpose of the stone was to get the diver swiftly to the seabed, where he would gather into a bag at his waist as many shellfish as he could, before his breath ran out.

Then he would 'slip his moorings' and return to the surface where other workers opened the shells in search of pearls. It was gey sair on the divers, that job, and it is most unlikely that they were well-paid.

60

'Twa horse tails? says the Pearl King, 'I think we wid manage that, but I'm nae so sure aboot the speyngie. But we'll see!'

'Wid ye like to bide for your supper?' says Mrs Birnie.

'Weel, seein' that ye insist, we'll bide!' says Deydie.

Boys! I'll never forget that supper. Biled eggs an' oat-cakes. What a treat! But what surprised me most was the fact that Mrs Birnie's hens could lay 'hale eggs! Peterheid hens could only lay halfs apparently. Ye're aye learnin'!

'Wid onybody like anither egg?' says Mrs Birnie.

'Aye surely!' says I, 'I could fairly go anither een'!

Deydie gied me a look like a summons. I'm thinkin' that wis 'cos I'd beaten him to the only egg that was left!

After tea Mr Birnie took us 'ben the hoose' where there was a great muckle roll-top desk. 'Noo, my loon' says he, 'In this thing there's some secret drawers that I'll let ye see'! Now I had seen a lot o' worsit drawers on the claes tows in the Blue Toon: I had often seen the type of wifie's drawers that were called 'open docks', and which must have been very draughty, but I had never seen secret drawers.

But my curiosity was soon satisfied when from a secret drawer Mr Birnie drew a little 'shammy-leather' baggie tied with a draw-string. 'Hud oot yer han's' says he, then into my cupped hands he poured the most beautiful pearls I have ever seen. Even tho' I was just a bairn I sensed that they were extra special! Perfection to the nth degree.

'Foo aul' are ye? asked the Pearl King. Then when I had replied he said 'Supposin' ye live till ye're a hunner 'ear aul' ye'll nivver earn the price o' fits in yer han's the day'! I ken noo he wis richt.

On the way home Deydie produced one of his gems when he remarked 'There's naething like an egg for a soor rift, littlin!' He did ither things besides riftin' till I was near scumfished! But since I was the proud bearer of two lovely horse tails, I said nothing.

Some time later, in April 1925, Mr Alexander Birnie presented to the town of Peterhead the Birnie Bridge which spans the Ugie near its mouth. Prior to the erection of the Brig the only access to the golf course and the beautiful beaches was by means of a flat-bottomed, square-ended coble which was drawn across the river on a wire rope slung from bank to bank.

The opening ceremony for the new Brig was a great occasion. The 'hale toon was there an' ivvery bairn got a chocolate egg. I got mine along wi' the lave but it could nivver match the egg I got in the Pearl King's hoose.

One mystery remains! For many, many years after the Brig was opened there was a penny fee to get across. Now, it is a stark fact that for most of these years a great many folk in Peterhead simply could not afford the penny. But times changed so that prosperity was the order of the day, then the charge was abolished!

It's enough to gi'e a boddy a soor rift!

A helpin' o' mustard for the maitre d'hotel

An observant traveller on the Peterhead-Aberdeen road can scarcely fail to observe that in the not too distant past a railway connected Boddam with Ellon.

The rails have long been removed but great lengths of embankment are still plainly visible, as are the great granite supports of several bridges, especially on the outskirts of the village of Cruden Bay. The line ran from Boddam to Cruden Bay to Hatton and thence to Ellon via Pitlurg and Auchmacoy.

The station-master's houses were all built of local granite to a standard pattern and to this day they are sturdy dwelling houses, one of which stands close alongside the main road at Longhaven. Improvements over the past twenty years have ironed out the notoriously dangerous kinks where the road was obliged to cross the railway (and vice-versa) but the younger generation could profitably spend a pleasant afternoon tracing the route of the old line.

I can well remember that the fences which bounded the line were ideal for the drying of fleets of herring nets during the immediate post-war years, when mile after mile of track was filled with decrepit and dilapidated rolling stock. Trucks and wagons of all kinds lay there for years awaiting repair until bit by bit they were taken south.

There was also the colossal Railway Hotel at Cruden Bay. Comprising 365 bedrooms it stood on the site which is now the Golf Club car park. The big granite building which still stands near the car park was in fact the laundry for the magnificent hotel which was a welcome source of employment for a veritable army of locals.

Many of the village boys earned a canny wage caddying for the host of wealthy golfers who came from far and near. One of the caddies, Bill Robertson (Weft), was the envy of his pals because he was the regular bag-carrier for Mr Colman, the mustard millionaire, who loved to holiday at Cruden Bay, where everybody knew that Mr Colman's millions came from the mustard which diners left on the edge of their plates.

Now, mustard is a pleasant condiment when it is used wisely. It lifts a humble dish such as hairy tatties to heights which T-bone steaks could never hope to reach. But mustard can be devastating!

In days of old, fisher weddings or 'mairridges' were simple, homely affairs where the wedding ceremony, the 'Feed' and the dance all took place under the same roof, usually a local hall. Indeed my own grandparents, Aul' Oxy fae Burnhaven an' Meggie Forman fae Buchanhaven each walked halfway, accompanied by their invited guests, to meet at the Ropework (now the Bayview Garage) where they were wed.

The floor had, of course, been cleared before-hand and everybody had a whale of a time, the feed being salt-fish an' tatties (hairy tatties) with mustard, a cut abeen the normal tatties an' herrin'! Of recent years, however, fisher mairridges have graduated to the five-star hotel level where no expense is spared and where female guests arrive dressed like 'parish models with incendiaries to tone'.

Picture, then, such a function in an illustrious establishment: the guests all busy at their caviar, when there appears on the scene an uninvited dog, a mongrel of huge proportions and a very friendly manner. Rather too friendly maybe, because it insists on sniffing at your anatomy where sniffs are definitely not allowed!

At first nobody says 'boo', 'cos ye see, it's maybe the skipper's dog, but an old shipmate of mine who knows better decides to cure this detestable sniffing habit, so, with the blade of his table knife as a sort of catapult he skites a great dollop of mustard onto the dog's beauty spot, which is immediately below the root of its tail!

The startled beast decides to investigate by bending itself into a semi-circle first to port, then to starboard without success, so not to be outdone, it contorts its body into a grotesque form so that the nose can sniff the offending substance. There is apparently no smell so it takes one almighty lick, then all hell breaks loose!

The demented beast, with its tongue and belly both on fire goes completely berserk, charging up and down the room like a hairy cannon ball and howling like a banshee, until a quick-thinking flunkey opens a French window and lets the demon escape.

Some sort of order is soon restored to the battlefield and everyone is about to resume operations when the bride's mother, resplendent in shantung silk an' fairly dreepin' wi' jewels, rises groggily to her feet, and gripping the table-edge so hard that her knuckles gleam white, she asks in a strained voice 'Quine! Faar's 'e watry?'

On receiving specific instructions she makes for the door with a peculiar gait, apparently desirous of haste and yet not quite able to attain it. She is followed in rapid succession by several other ladies, all suddenly and obviously cripple. Powerful stuff, mustard!

The mustard king, Mr Colman, dearly loved to visit the harbour at Port Errol, a place which is known to fishermen as 'The Ward'. There he had a close friend in Weelum Tait, a local fisherman of forthright speech. Older readers may remember his appearance on TV when he beat the Panel in 'What's my Line', the panel being Gilbert Harding, Anona Wynn and Isobel Barnett.

The millionaire liked nothing better than to sit on the side-deck of Weelum's boatie, the *Posy*, with his bare feet trailing in the sea while the boatie was underway and many a time did he foregather, with a few titled personages, in the kitchen of Weelum's hoosie (directly opposite the Lady's Briggie) to feast on Granny Tait's breid (oatcakes).

One fine morning, desirous of a sail in the boat, he came to the harbour, only to learn that there wis 'ower muckle motion, ye wid only get weet'! Rather disappointed, he decided that he would gi'e Weelum a hurl in his Rolls Royce limousine. Weelum required no second bid so, just as he stood, he boarded the great vehicle, sitting in the rear seat with the millionaire while the chauffeur acted as pilot.

Lunch-time found them parked outside the Invercauld Arms at Braemar. Mr Colman had with him a packed lunch which he shared with his chauffeur but there was not sufficient for Weelum who, apart from being very hungry, was also stoney broke, a situation which was promptly remedied with a pound note from the rich man's wallet. 'Go and have a nice meal in the hotel, Weelum!'

So our hero, impervious to the frosty stares of the other diners, seated himself at a window table, tossing his caip onto the window sill. He was immediately informed by a saucy waitress that this was the first-class dining room, no place for any person in fisherman's garb.

'Weel!' says Weelum, 'Ye'll need to unnerstan' that I'm a first-class gentleman an' I'm needin' a first-class denner!'

This merely hastened the arrival of the maitre-d'hotel who was determined to have this fisher lout thrown out until Weelum, pointing to the Rolls outside the window asked 'Div ye ken fa' that is?'

Of course the mannie kent it wis Mr Colman. 'Weel, it wis him that sent me in here for my denner an' if I dinna get it he'll see till't that ye dinna get nae mair mustard!'

At that moment the millionaire glanced towards the window and, sensing Weelum's predicament, he gave him a reassuring wave but simultaneously he raised a very expressive eyebrow at the chief flunkey. So Weelum got his denner!

'Man, Peter,' says he to me, 'Yon wis the best feed I ivver saw. If it wis on the menu, I took it, twa doses o' some things until I wis fit to burst. But ye ken the aul' sayin' – "Better belly-rive than gweed mait spiled"! An' to feenish aff I had a glass o' the finest fuskie! I gied the lassie the powen note an' she cam' back wi' my change in a silver dishie. "Och, quine!" says I, "Keep the change!" Fit wis three half-croons to the likes o' me? I felt like a millionaire!'

'A mustard millionaire, Weelum?' says I with a laugh.

'Ye could say that, Peter! Mustard's powerfu' stuff, ye ken!'

Getting to grips with the coggie

Prior to the last war, the big Fifie herring boats were a common sight on the east coast of Scotland.

Most of them had been built before the turn of the century, purely and simply as sailing vessels without any kind of machinery whatsoever apart from a hand-driven winch which was called the Iron Man. This winch was used to haul the heavy messenger rope and was always sited well aft because in those days the boats lay by the stern at their nets.

The invention of the steam capstan was a great step forward. The capstan took the heavy strains off the crew in the hauling of the rope and the handling of the rigging.

Since the practice was still to lie by the stern, the capstan was still sited well aft and the upright boiler was placed in the cabin where the crew ate and slept. Fancy that!

Many years later, another great invention, the internal combustion engine, appeared on the scene, most of the boats opting for the 75 h.p. Gardner paraffin engine.

And where did they put the engine? In the cabin, of course!

It had to be heated with blowlamps before it would start so you can see that the cabin could be a most unpleasant place. The crew's bedding and clothing stank of paraffin and their food was tainted, although seasoned motor boat men didn't seem to notice!

Sailboats had no wheelhouse. Such a thing was not possible owing to the rig of the sails.

The motor engine changed all that. The entire rig of the boats was changed and it was possible to dispense with the three-ton fore mast and the two-ton mizzen mast and replace them with much lighter spars.

So now we have a wheelhouse which can hold two men and an engine with a reverse gear which is controlled from the deck by means of a key exactly the same as that which plumbers use to shut off the water from your house.

We're gettin' on jist fine fin along comes the Board o' Trade an' says: 'Boys, it's time ye had a sma' boat!' 'Faar are we gaun t' pit it?' says you. 'Pit it faar ye like, but ye hiv t' get it!' says the Board.

I know for a fact that most of these sma' boats were never moved from the day they were installed, being gradually glued to their chocks with countless coats of paint!

For some obscure reason, the old sail or motor boats had no toilet at all. There was a communal 'coggie', a small wooden cask which before use had to be partly filled with water and after use had to be immediately emptied overboard.

'Ye darna wyte a meenit or the thing wid cowp an' that wid be a gey job!'

Now, one lovely summer day in 1939, a boat such as I have described was heading east-by-north from Peterhead.

She was one of a great fleet seeking the shoals o' herrin' and, although none of her crew knew it, this would be her last year at the fishing. She would sail no more after the Hitler war.

Except for the helmsman, the crew were in their bunks and all was peace and quiet. Then, about 4 p.m., Hector, a veteran deckie, left his bunk to obey the call of nature.

For a minute or two he sat beside his bunk filling his pipe. From his bunk at the bottom of the ladder, Francie, the young cook, watched Hector go through his normal routine.

Francie knew that Hector would spurn the coggie, and would take up a position on the port quarter, outside the sma' boat whose gunnel he would grasp as he crouched in a really classical pose, with the North Sea as the coggie that couldna' cowp.

Francie also hated the coggie and only lack of nerve kept him from doing as Hector did. What if a foot or a hand should slip?

But today he would ha'e a lookie to see where Hector placed his feet, so, in his stocking soles the loon crept up the ladder and, without actually leaving the hatch at all, he peeped round the stern o' the sma' boat.

What a shock he got! He clean forgot to look at Hector's feet for there, about two feet away, Hector's lily-white stern was in full view along with his badge-of-office.

On a sudden and irresistible impulse the coorse nickum on the ladder reached forth and gave the inoffensive morsel a good hearty 'Toot' before vanishing down the ladder and into his bunk.

Poor Hector opened his mouth to yell and immediately lost his pipe overboard. Simultaneously, he sprang to attention like any guardsman while, as part of the same movement, he attempted to vault right across the sma' boat.

But, since his feet had got fanned up wi' his breeks, his style was somewhat cramped and he landed with a fearsome crash face down amongst the oars and the brooms and the buckets and the jam jars for which the sma' boat made such a handy receptacle.

'Fit on earth's wrang wi' ye, Hector?' demanded the skipper.

'A beast o' some kind took hud o' me. There! said Hector, pointing a tarry forefinger, but feart to look.

'Weel!' said the mate who had knelt down to make a close inspection, 'It couldna' been a shark or there wid ha'e been teethmarks!'

'Teethmarks!' cried the skipper, 'If it had been a shark there widna' been naething! Hap yersel', Hector, there's naething wrang wi' ye!'

The skipper was no fool! Fit wye had Francie nae come up wi' the rest? Like a shot the skipper made for the cabin and tore the blankets off the boy who was lying convulsed with laughter.

At supper the topic was sharks, Moby Dick and sea monsters.

The unsuspecting Hector asked, as he held oot his plate for mair sassidges, 'Francie, my loon, you that's new awa' fae the school, div 'ee ken fit could ha'e teen a hud o' me the day?'

'Fit wye wid I ken?' was the reply, 'But gaun b' the noise ye made it could ha'e been the propellor!'

Hard, hot summer days at the herrin'

There is an old saying that an Orcadian is a crofter with a boat but a Shetlander is a fisherman with a croft. There is quite a difference!

Over the years the Shetland men have prosecuted the fishing far more vigorously than their Orcadian brethren, and during the reign of King Herring, Lerwick was an important centre indeed.

During the summer months the local fleet, crewed by men whose ancient Norse links were still strong and whose language was more or less their own, was augmented by herring drifters from all over the east coast of Scotland.

And, of course, there was the annual arrival of a strong contingent of English boats, mostly from East Anglia. So Lerwick was and always has been a cosmopolitan centre where every fisher accent imaginable could be heard on a Saturday night.

As a rule the herring shoals appeared first in Shetland waters before moving south along the east coast to finish up in the autumn off East Anglia.

The scientist fellas were at great pains to tell the fishermen that these were not the same shoals at all, but different fish altogether, comprising different age groups, etc.

For many years the fishermen paid no heed. 'Fa wid listen 'til a chiel that said "Veeking Bank" instead o' "Viking Bank" an' him come o' fisher folk himsel'?'

Modern fishermen do listen to scientists but in those days they just laughed at them. 'Oh, what know they of harbours who toss not on the sea?' (Radford). Same sentiments!

During the early part of the Shetland herring season the sea took on a cloudy, brownish hue. This the fishers called the 'growth'. But as the season advanced the same waters would turn as white as milk.

Herring nets which had been used in such waters appeared, on being dried, as if they had been dusted with flour! The fishers didn't like the 'fite watter' simply because the herrings disliked it too.

Herring drifters based on Lerwick called at Lerwick proper with their catches. There the catch was sold but the boat would leave immediately for the buyer's curing station which could be three or four miles away.

These curing stations were scattered up and down the Sound, many of them being on the Isle of Bressay. Each station had its own wharf with its set of rails for the bogies, which carried the herrings from the boat to the yard.

Of course, all the pushing had to be done by the deckies, hard sweaty work on a hot summer day, especially since it was always uphill!

At the curing stations the guttin' quines or weemin (never 'girls') would yoke to the gutting of the herring.

Three quines to a crew, two gutting and one packing, they had been transported to Shetland at their employers' expense on the deck of the steamer from Aberdeen.

That's richt, freen! On the deck! And it's nae aye a summer day tho' it's summer time!

The quines dreaded crossing the 'Roost', a particularly nasty stretch of sea which draws its coorseness from the strong tides which sweep between Orkney and Shetland.

In their hundreds the quines 'manned' the curing yards. Drawn from every fishing village from Wick to Peterhead they worked long hard hours in the open air at what was really slave labour.

Their accommodation consisted of wooden huts furnished with two-tier bunks and precious little else. Cooking facilities were primitive as were also the sanitary arrangements. In these huts the quines had to fend for themselves.

For the coopers a female cook was employed. There could be other men apart from the coopers for some curers employed a few Irishmen as gutters who could also be utilised as labourers. The cook looked after them too.

Since most of the curers had stations or yards in the mainland ports, they could follow the herring shoals all the way south to Yarmouth. And since the quines were required there also, there was a continuous migration of fisher folk pursuing the silver darlin's, men, women and often bairns forbye.

Ye'll mind on John, my pal wi' the great muckle plook

on his neck? Then ye'll mind that he was actually a cooper to trade.

When he furhooied the trawling he returned to his coopering and one particularly hot summer he was gaffer on a curing station on Bressay.

Since there was never any Sunday fishing there were no herrings to be gutted on Mondays, so Monday forenoon was spent 'filling up' the barrels from the previous week's cure.

This meant topping up any barrels whose contents had settled somewhat; additional pickle or brine was poured in via the bunghole and this task kept all hands busy till dinner time. Monday afternoon was the 'half-day'.

Well now, this particular Monday it was the cook's birthday so she had laid on a super-dooper feed for her 'boys'. The menu could hardly be described as a 'summer' one; Scotch Broth with or without duff, boiled beef an' tatties with or without duff, rice and raisins with prunes followed by tay an' cheesecakes.

John was a very hard worker with a splendid appetite so he stuffed himself till he was fit to burst, then he stytered oot o' the hut to lie face down in the heather beneath the broiling sun. There he promptly fell asleep.

A few moments later the cook came outside to work at her pots and pans, and on seeing John's vulnerability, a gleam of unholy glee illumined her eye.

With the broth pot in one hand and the pudden dish in the other she waltzed gaily across the heathery slope to dowp herself doon on John's spine – all sixteen stone of her sonsie Irish frame.

The immediate result was a tremendous explosion in John's innards. Baith his een skited oot; it's a mercy they came back! Peys came down his nose and cheesecake very nearly choked him.

He never heard the simultaneous eruption at his opposite end because particles of duff were looking for an exit via his lugs; but there was no denying that such an event had taken place!

The hallarackit quine didn't realise that she could have killed poor John. To her the whole episode was a great joke, altho' on this occasion she was obliged to wash his shift for him. Well, somebody had to do it!

What surprised me most was the fact that through it all John's strongest words were 'Ooh me! Ooh me! I dinna like the Irish'!

Dinna eat cheese wi' green bitties!

Not until he was stowing his stores in the cabin locker did Jeemsie discover the little parcel, and by that time the *Meadowsweet* had cleared the breakwater.

'Fitivver this is, it's nae oors, an' the smell says it's time it wis ower the side!' And with that he made for the deck.

In the galley he bumped into Duncan, his bosom pal. 'Fit's 'at ye hiv, Jeemsie?'

'Gweed kens, Duncan! I hinna heen a richt look yet, but I think it's hairy-mouldit cheese, so I'll dump it!'

'Lat's ha'e a look,' says Duncan, then, 'Ye canna dump that, my loon. It's cheese a'richt, but it's nae hairy-mouldit ava! That's the kine o't! I dinna mine the richt name o't, but it soun's like Gordon's College an' it smells like the skipper's feet!

'I think it micht be richt gweed wi' a bittie breid (oatcake). Some peer wifie's gaun t' miss her tasty bite the nicht. Fit aboot a tinkie's maskin' for the twa o's, an' we'll try this fancy cheese!'

So the twa heroes partook of a delectable snack while the rest of the crew, apart from the helmsman, were in the land of Nod. Gorgonzola cheese on a drifter? It'll be blue snaa neist!

Duncan enjoyed the rare treat, but Jeemsie wisna ower happy. 'It's the green bitties that I dinna like, Duncan! I'm sure this stuff'll gar my sark tail crack like a wheep. I'm awa' t' see if I can catch her (have a nap) for an hour afore supper time!'

'Away ye go, my loon. I'll sweel oot the twa joogs!' says his pal.

So in a few minutes Jeemsie was horizontal on his caffsaick, readin' 'The Coral Island' by his favourite author R. M. Ballantyne.

But soon the book dropped from his limp fingers and the lad was away in dreamland, on the bonniest beach he had ever seen. The sea was as blue as the een o' yon quine in the grocer's shop!

But fit wye wis the *Meadowsweet* stuck oot there on the coral reef wi' nivver a sign o' life? An' fit wis a' this wreckage on the bonny fite san'? An' far wis a'body onywye?

'A'body's lost, Jeemsie! We're the only twa that's left! We'll jist ha'e t' mak' the best o't!' This from Duncan, who had suddenly appeared on the scene. 'I'm thinkin' the sharks got them!'

'Eh! The peer aul' Turk, Duncan! Aswarn the shark that taikled him has a gey sair belly noo!'

'Nivver mine the Turk!' says Duncan, 'Ging 'ee along the san' an' gaither a puckle sticks t' licht a firie. I see palm trees at the heid o' the beach, an' far there's palms there's yams. I'll ging up an ha'e a howk!'

'Fit on earth's yams, Duncan?'

'Things like tatties, but bigger. I see the tattie pot's been washen ashore so we'll manage t' bile the things! We canna live on the win' an' chaw daylicht!'

'Could ye nae fess back a puckle coconuts, Duncan?'

'First things first my loon! Get 'ee the fire goin'!'

In a very short time Jeemsie had managed to rake from the wreckage the tattie-pot, twa packets o' fat, half a dizzen loafs that wid seen dry in the sun, an' a packet o' fardins (butter biscuits).

He had gotten the fire t' licht efter a sair tyauve ('cos ye see, the sticks wis weet) fin Duncan came back wi' 's airms full o' bonny big yams.

'We'll bile them wi' their jackets on, Jeemsie, usin' sea water for the saat!'

'I'd raither ha'e chips, Duncan! Could we nae ha'e chips? I'm affa fond o' chips! There's plinty o' fat!'

'A'richt, my loon we'll ha'e chips, but I'm nae ower fond o' chips b' themsel's, so I'll ging into the jungle an' see if I can get a bittie o' kitchie.

'Chips need kitchie, specially the chips that 'ee mak'. They're like bits o' foggy neep. I micht get a turtle or an armadillo or an iguana, ye nivver ken!'

'I'm tellin' ye, Duncan, if ye come back wi' an elephant ye'll ha'e t' skin the thing yersel'!'

So Duncan disappeared into the dense jungle, leaving Jeemsie to peel and slice the yams and to get the fat boiling hot.

Quarter of an hour later Jeemsie couldna believe his

ee'n! Here wis Duncan comin' wallopin' doon the beach, trailin' a little darkie loon b' the hair o' the heid!

'Far did ye get the likes o' him, Duncan?'

'In the jungle, ye gowk! There's nae anither livin' thing t' be seen. Nae lizards, nae even a cobra! Nae naething!'

'An' fit are we gaun t' dee wi' 'im, Duncan?'

'Och! We'll roast 'im, my loon! I believe he wid be richt gweed wi' chips.'

Ye'll ha'e t' kill the craitur first, though, won't ye?'

'Na, na, my loon, that wid be cruel!'

'An' fit wye div ye roast a darkie loon, Duncan?'

'Nae bother ava, my loon. We'll mak' a spit wi' some o' that broken timmer an' we'll lash the loon on-till't, an' if ye keep turnin' 'im slow he'll cook jist gran'!

'The same fire 'll dee the chips an' the roast at the same time, but if ye turn the spit ower fast he winna cook richt.

'I canna be deein' wi' mait that's nae richt teen aboot, so turn 'im slow, slow! I'm awa' back t' the jungle for some fruit. I like a bittie o' dessert efter my denner!'

'Mine an' fess a coconut, Duncan!'

It wisna lang afore Duncan wis back wi' a great muckle bunch o' bananas on his shooder, an' boys, he fairly got a begick, for Jeemsie wis garrin' the spit furl like the verra haimmers!

'Hey! Fit div ye think ye're deein'? cries Duncan. 'He'll nivver cook at that speed! I tellt ye t' furl 'im slow, slow!'

'So ye did!' says Jeemsie. I wis furlin' 'im fine an' canny so that he wid be fine an' broon, but ilkie time he came roon' he wis takin' a hanfae o' chips oot o' the pot!'

Nivver again did Jeemsie look at cheese wi' green bitties in't!

A swarm o' locusts attacked the wreck!

'Fog, to fairmers, is mist.' To fishermen it is 'thickness', and according to its density, it can be thick, smore thick, tar thick or as thick as guts, the latter variety being rather opaque.

The Buchan coast is renowned for dense fog and, in the days before echo sounders and radar were known, many a gallant ship came to grief on this north-east shoulder of Scotland.

One such casualty was the *City of Osaka*, which met her end close to the cliffs just south of the Scaurs o' Cruden in a bight where Buchan Ness Light is not visible and 'Boddam Coo' seldom heard. As thick as guts? Aye! Surely!

The sea was calm and the crew of thirty-two were safely disembarked by the Peterhead lifeboat, leaving the great ship silent and deserted, hopelessly fast on the rocks. No sooner had the unfortunate mariners been landed than a peculiar fever smote the sma'-boat fraternity in the Blue Toom.

Pilots and poachers by profession, and pirates by descent they had been reared on tales of past wrecks such as the *Union* and the *Princess Mary* whose legendary cargoes had proved to be a heaven-sent windfall for the Buchan fisher folk.

Indeed, every man-jack kent somebody that had 'an organ or a shewin' machine or great wobs-o-claith-in-aneth-the-bed.

'In fact ae wifie had a 'hale tea-set wi' floories on't an' far div ye think she got that?

'An' far did she get the lame (china) chuntie-pot to match? Oot o' a wreck! Far ither could she get sic gran' gear?'

And so the fever spread until, with a slight lifting of the fog curtain there came a mass exodus of ripper boats from the port of Peterhead.

Anything from 18 to 30 feet, these clinker biggit boaties had Kelvin paraffin engines and they raced each other for the prize of being first aboard the wreck. Well, after all, didn't the old hymn say 'Where treasure calls, or plunder, be never wanting there!'

Every member of the pirate gang was well versed in the laws of salvage. 'If it's lowse, ye can tak' it! If it's fast to the ship ye daurna tak' it, 'cos that's stealin'!'

Now this term 'fast to the ship' covered things like engines and bilers, winches an' twa-ton anchors, so there was a vast expanse of territory which was quite legal.

Of course the Receiver of Wrecks and the Police were quite unaware of these loopholes in the law but then they were ignorant folk that didna ken ony better.

Leading the flotilla was the ripper boat *Gem* skippered by the Chemist, a chiel who had in his youth spent a summer wi' his mither's folk in Fife.

On his return he had spurned the word 'Droggist' which was the north-east term, preferring the title Chemist when he was sent for a Seidlitz pooder. Hence his nickname. His crew were his twa loons, Dod and Bill.

As they neared the wreck Dod says 'Da! Wid there be a pianna aboord there? Ma wid afa like a pianna!'

'Fit on earth wid she dee wi' a pianna?' says his Da. 'She has mair need o' a tay-pot an' a kettle so mak' for the galley at yer hardest! An' you, Bill, it's the wheelhouse for you. I could dee fine wi' a pair o' binoculars!'

The Chemist ran his boatie smartly alongside the rope ladder which the crew had used to board the lifeboat, and the boys swarmed aboard.

Boat after boat arrived a few minutes later and the ship was invaded by a mob of looters who stripped her bare in a matter of minutes.

I'm tellin' ye, a bourachie o' Bluemogganers could tak' a swarm o' locusts an' learn them a lesson or twa!

Young Dod had struck it rich in the galley and soon he was lowering into the boatie the biggest copper kettle he had ever seen.

This was rapidly followed by several buckets of odds an' sods, cutlery, mugs, packets o' tay an' tins o' coffee. 'That's the stuff, my loon! See fit else ye can get noo!' cried his Da.

Suddenly there came a despairing shout from Bill on the bridge. 'Da! There's naething left! I'm thinkin' there's been a puckle thiefs here!'

'Thiefs? Far could they ha'e come fae? I thocht we wis

first here! See if ye can get the steerin' wheel aff; 'twid mak' a richt fine gatie for the back-close!'

'The wheel's awa' an' a' Da!'

'Good grief!' says the Chemist. 'Well, dinna waste time! Try somewye else. Hist ye clivver fast!'

Great sighs of regret arose to the heavens when the pirates, on opening the hatches, discovered some 15 feet of water in the holds. There was no cargo within reach. What a shame!

Meantime Dod had discovered the paint store whence he had obtained six 5-gallon drums of paint and several brushes.

'I hope the tins wis open fin ye got them!' cried the Chemist anxiously.

'No, Da! They warna! But they're open noo! That mak's them legal disn't it?'

'That's ma boy! Ye're fairly learnin'! Lower them doon canny my loon. It widnae dee t' sink the yole!'

Since the crew, apart from the officers, had all been poor Lascars, their living quarters yielded very little. Indeed every one of them had boarded the lifeboat with a pathetic little bundle aneth his oxter.

But the Chemist did see his next-door neeber wi' a hubble-bubble pipe which was to prove 'As sair on tobacco as a drifter is on coal!'

Now Bill, anxious to emulate his brither, had discovered a clothing store and came to the ships' rail with a bale of jerseys on his shooder.

The bale landed with a thump on the boaties deck. 'I'll be back in a meenit wi' some boots, Da!' he cried.

Suddenly a keen-eyed loon in the bows shouted 'A.B.C.R.L.!' (a bobby comin', rin lads) and in a matter of seconds the pirates had abandoned the ship and were off for home with their loot.

'I see the bobby on the tap o' the cliff!' says the Chemist. 'It maun be the Collieston bobby, 'cos there's nae een in Finnyfaul'.'

As the *Gem* entered the bay at Peterheid an honest citizen fishing from the breakwater shouted a warning. 'Dinna ging into the hairber, lads! The bobbies is doon like bum-bees searchin' ilkie boatie!'

So the Chemist immediately altered course and ran the *Gem* into the Garron, a rocky inlet on the back side of the Queenie.

There the treasure was unloaded, carried across the rocks to the pier at Greenhill and dropped into the foc'sle of the drifter *Coronet* near the old lifeboat shed.

Of course the *Gem* was searched on entering harbour. Clean bill of health!

After supper the loons widna rest till they got the stuff hame but their father advised caution. 'Better let it lie for a day or twa!'

'It'll be a' stolen if we wyte ower lang! There's a lot o' thiefs on the go, ye ken!' says Bill, near greetin'.

So down went the heroes to the *Coronet's* foc'sle where they held a council of war. 'Fit wye div we get it hame?'

'Weel,' says the Chemist. 'The ganjies is gaun hame! The rest o' the stuff can wyte!'

Thereupon he donned ganjie after ganjie till he was like an advert for Michelin tyres. In fact he couldna get his airms doon t' his sides, there wis that mony fauls aneth his oxters!

'Da!' says Dod, lachin', 'Ye'll nivver get up the road like that! Ye're like a great muckle penguin. "Melodian-hips," the bobby, he'll spot ye a mile awa!'

'Nivver een!' says the Chemist. 'Leave that to me!'

So, stepping onto the pier, he got a loon on either side and with his arms across their shooders he assumed a very painful limp and trauchled hamewith.

At the Brig 'Melodian-hips' surveyed the trio with concern. 'Fit's happened, skipper? Are ye sair hurtit?'

'Och! I've geen ower my fitt, constable, but wi' the twa loons I'll manage hame. It's gey sair a' the same!'

'I see that!' says the bobby. 'It's fairly garrin ye swyte!'

Thus were the ganjies brought home. The rest of the swag was retrieved in small doses over several days.

It's a lang time noo since the Chemist passed on but the sons are still to the fore. They can be seen onyday at the Lazy Dyke and they are aye dressed in bonny navy ganjies. For mair than fifty 'ear they've been like that!

Now, should you, a stranger, enquire politely of these gentlemen, 'Fit like's the Blue Toon noo wi' a' the fish an' the coal an' the fertiliser an' the gas an' the ile?' they'll shak' their grey heids and tell ye wi' the greet in their throats.

'It's nae the same, freen, nae the same! It's an afa place for thiefs noo!'

Sad tale of the Caley bannock

There's naething so queer as folk! In saying such a thing I cannot honestly exclude my ain folk, the fishermen. And why not?

Well now, there's something about fishermen, of whom I am one, that I have never fully understood and it's this – should one of their number forsake the sea to try his hand at some venture on shore then every eye is upon him.

Should his bold attempt prove to be hopeless failure, it is simply because his innate honesty and lack of guile have proved to be inadequate weaponry in his battle with the sharks who infest the shore.

If, on the other hand, his foray into a foreign clime proves to be a resounding success then it's 'just what a boddy might have expected for hadn't he been a droll hare all his days? Ye ken! Yon kind o' lad that would kick ye in the belly when your back was turned!'

So how can a fella win?

One outstanding example of a fisherman quitting the sea to make a real impact on shore was the late Robert Forman, O.B.E., J.P., who finished up a Provost of Peterhead.

In the early thirties he founded a business under the name of Caledonian Fishselling Co. which was never known as anything else but 'The Caley', just as he himself was never known as anything else but Rob Forman.

The motto was 'Caley for Service' and I'm sure he did his utmost to live up to that motto. Many successful fishermen of the fifties owed their success in great measure to the shrewdness, the encouragement and support of Rob Forman.

The cynic might say 'Well! In helping others he was helping himself!'

In reply I would say 'Why not? How many businessmen do you know who are charitable institutions?'

The Caley in its early days was a very small concern, but it grew steadily over the years to become Caley Fisheries Group.

My earliest recollection of Rob Forman is the day he accosted me at the harbour with the query, 'Fit's you sma'-boat men deein' this winter?' This would be about 1934. 'Och!' says I, 'We're at the lug lines, sair made to get a livin' '.

'Oor bait has to come from Ardersier an' it disnae come here till the late train comes in an' even then there's times it disna turn up. Then we're lowsed!'

'That's lack o' organisation,' says Rob. 'Tell a' the sma'-boat men nae to order ony mair lug. I'll see that there's a steady supply an' if ye're needin' bait jist come to the Caley for't.'

So instead of ordering our bait by telegram we would just go to the Caley store at any time and get our biscuit tin of lug.

Now it came to pass that the Lord sent a mighty south-east wind so that the waters wrought exceedingly. Great seas marched across the bay, like an army of giants, to commit suicide on the foreshore and on Smith's Embankment.

The breakwaters were visible only at rare intervals. Every boat was securely moored in the inner harbour and the storm-booms were in position at the Queenie Brig.

For a 'hale stricken week the gale continued and so did the steady supply of bait. A south-east storm keeps the Buchan fleet in port but it has no effect at Ardersier. So every night at 8.50 a fresh consignment of biscuit tins arrived by train to be conveyed on a hurley to the Caley store pending the abatement of the storm.

The general welfare of the worms was left in the hands of Jeemsie Bruce who at that time was the Caley's runner-cum-factotum-cum-paraffin man. His boss had given strict orders that under no circumstances could the beasties be allowed to perish because dead worms catch no cod.

Some bright spark advised Jeemsie to spread the worms on a floor then scatter them with the bitties o' cork that ye get in grape barrels. This Jeemsie did, but in spite of his efforts the mortality rate was very high and soon he was at his wits end.

At the height of the storm several fishermen were pacing to-and-fro in the old fishmarket discussing the weather and generally setting the world to rights. They formed an illustrious gathering including Katie Andra and Chielsie Tug (Choice), Nep's Robert (Snowflake), Gordon's Andra (Recruit), Tondin's Jock (Annie Elizabeth) and Twull's Andrickie (Jeannie). There were also present our late lamented friends the Taylor brothers who were pilots, known world-wide as the Wells o' Wearie, this being their theme song when they had imbibed rather liberally.

There were others too numerous to mention, and then of course, there was myself, a young feel loon whose retentive memory was busy gleaning from the wisdom of these old salts, a vast store of knowledge which, in later years, was to prove absolutely worthless!

Suddenly, Jeemsie Bruce appeared, crying in deepest anguish, 'For God's sake boys, come and see this!'

We followed him en masse to the Caley store to witness a scene which I shall never forget. Imagine a bannock of sharn fifteen feet square and four inches deep, then give it a smell ten times worse than the vilest odour you have ever encountered and you will have a faint idea of what we had been called upon to witness.

Forty tins of dead and dying lug worms with their liberal mixture of cork! I was deeply impressed when, in the presence of so much death, each man removed his bonnet, until I realised that the bonnets were being used as gas masks. Then I regretted that I was bareheaded.

With our backs hard to the wall we stood around the room while Jeemsie held aloft an acetylene lamp to illuminate the scene. He reminded me somehow of the Statue of Liberty.

'Fit am I gaun t' dee wi' this sotter?' he cried. 'The Boss'll fyle himsel' if I lat them dee!'

Silence reigned for a moment then a one-eyed sage remarked: 'The best thing to dee Jeemsie, would be to mak' pies wi' them!' Great hilarity as we made our exit!

Late that night the seething mass of corruption was shovelled into the harbour.

Many years later, during one of my many bouts of friendly banter with Provost Forman, I heard him elaborate on the benefits of organisation.

When I asked him, innocently: 'Div ye ken far I micht get a tin o' lug?' he suddenly remembered that he had urgent business elsewhere.

Black beasties that bring golden reward

The lug worm is not a beautiful sight. It is a fat, black beastie which makes its home in the sandy bottoms of estuaries or sheltered beaches, where it betrays its presence by leaving little heaps of droppings on the sands around low-water mark.

If you dig a hole on the seaward side of these little heaps, you'll find the lug which, despite its appearance, makes a wonderful bait.

Now, to obtain a few lug for an evening's angling is not a major problem, but should you require several hundred to bait a fleet of small lines the problem becomes acute and you'll have to 'send awa' ' for lug in bulk.

The best place to get lug is Ardersier, where extensive mudflats make a perfect lug nursery.

So you send a telegram to the mannie at Ardersier. Post-haste he will send you a biscuit tin full of lug which you must collect at Peterhead station where they will arrive on the last train at 8.50 p.m.

The cost will probably stagger you, for, including the telegram and the freight charges, your McVitties tin of worms will cost no less than twenty-three shillings! How can you be expected to make a living with bait at such a price?

Well, that's your own problem, so you just have to carry the bait home where the lines are ready for baiting.

But I almost forgot that during the day you've been busy getting a bucket of limpets from the rocks.

The best tool for 'hacking' limpets is an old straight-backed table knife with the handle well bound in flannel to ensure a good grip. This tool you will call a 'sprod' and, like countless others before you were born, you'll make the fatal mistake of holding your sprod like a dagger.

Sure, you'll dislodge the limpet at the first fell swipe but in so doing you'll skin your knuckles on the barnacles, which were invented for the express purpose of drawing blood.

You'll soon get the knack but it will take you a long time to fill a bucket of limpets, especially if several other folks are on the rocks after the same errand.

How to get the beasties out of their shells?

Plot them, you silly!

Pour boiling water over them and they'll fairly loup oot! But first you've to carry them home to join the lug.

Baiting the lines is a slow, painstaking job. You'll coil the line neatly into a wooden 'backet', laying the baited hooks in neat rows so that they will run clear during the shooting process. And between the rows you'll put strips of newspaper to keep the hooks apart.

It will take till nearly midnight for you and your mates to bait the six lines, comprising 1,200 hooks. The bait will be lug and limpet alternately, or 'time aboot', and when the job is finished you'll wash your stinking hands with Lysol before having a cup of tea.

Then it's off to sea to shoot the lines in the bitter cold of a winter morning. You'll be in a small boat whose only lights are paraffin lamps or the glare from a 'torch', which is like a kettle with a wide spout from which several strands of twisted wick protrude.

The fuel, of course, is paraffin. You'll have to be very careful because the boatie will do her best to pitch you overboard and there's not a great deal of room. You'll need to watch your fingers, too, because the lines are run out while the boat is forging rapidly ahead and the fresh wind can send the lethal hooks in strange directions.

If all goes well you may be back in harbour at 3 a.m. and you'll be free to sleep till six o'clock when you've got to be on your feet again.

You see, you've got these lines to haul and so you must be looking for your little flag buoy at the crack of dawn.

Hauling the lines is a slow business at best, but if you're lucky you may be home for dinner, probably a late one, then you'll land your few boxes of fish for the 4 p.m. sale.

That would be your day's work done but the lines have to be redd in preparation for tonight and that'll take you an hour or two. And possibly you've forgotten that you have another bucket of limpets to get, and haven't you to meet the train tonight to collect your lug?

When do you sleep? Mostly on your feet because you and your bed are strangers. If you are to work 100 hours in a six-day week you can only sleep in snatches, but when codlings are fetching as high as twelve shillings a box you've got to keep going.

Thus the 1930s, when a pound could purchase such a lot – if only you could get the pound.

My most vivid memory of those days is the time when I was landed on the pier in the dark of a winter morning while my shipmates went back to sea to haul the lines.

I had a hook embedded so deeply in my finger that neither my mates nor I could get it out. Most of the hook was out of sight in my flesh so I had to see the doctor.

Not wishing to disturb the good man so early, I waited till daylight before ringing the bell at the surgery in Queen Street.

Dr Taylor, in his dressing gown, admitted me, ushered me into his consulting room, then had a look at my finger.

'I think we'll manage to sort that,' says he, 'but I'll need to get the lassie to hud yer han' '.

'Och!' says I, I'm nae seekin' a quine here ava!'

But he paid no heed and summoned the maid from the lobby where she was busy with her brush. No hoovers in those days!

He showed the girl how to keep my finger rigid by using her own forefinger and thumb. Of course she could turn her head away if she wanted! Then he set to work with a scalpel and laid my finger open to the bone before he could remove the hook. Oh boys! It was sair!

'Ye can let go noo,' he said to the girl, who bolted like a flash.

Then to me he said: 'Ye'd better tak' the heuk hame wi' ye. It's ower big for my kind o' fishin'.'

Then the kindly man took me home. That was the first time I had a hurl in a car.

Good old days? Ye must be jokin'!

Do it on a fine day next time!

It was early afternoon on Saturday, August 4, 1962, and I was busy preparing the car for a jaunt wi' the wife an' the bairn.

It had been blowing a real gale during the night and indeed it was still blowing hard, but I wasn't particularly interested because I had quit the sea for good.

After several months ashore I was realising that, no matter how much you know about boats and engines and fish, you are on a sticky wicket when it comes to seeking a shore job, particularly when you are 45.

But I was determined to give it a real trial, and with such thoughts in mind I was lowering the car bonnet, when I glanced down the street. From the point where I stood only a narrow strip of sea was visible, but in that same narrow sector I could see two PD boats steering approximately north-east.

'Something funny here,' I thought. 'Awa' t' sea on Setterday efterneen! Some folk winna tak' time t' live!'

Within a minute I saw another boat and yet another, then I realised that it wasn't 'something funny' but something wrong that was on the go, so, after shouting to the wife that I would be back shortly, I set out on foot for the harbour.

There I saw boat after boat letting go and putting to sea, but I couldn't find anyone to tell me the reason why until, at the Cross Keys corner, I bumped into Tom Strachan, skipper of the *Silver Hope*.

'Faar are 'ee makkin' for the day?' says he. 'Ye're dressed like a circus horse!'

'Och!' says I, 'I'm for the country places! Fit's a' the maneer aboot, onywye?'

'Nae an afa lot. Jist the *Daisy's* crew in a liferaft a hunner-an'-forty mile aff.'

Only half believing him, I fired back: 'Fit's adee that ee're nae awa' wi' the lave?'

'Nae driver!' says Tam, 'I've a muster o' a kind, but there's nae a driver to be gotten!'

'I'll be back in five meenits,' says I, 'Ye've a driver noo!'

It transpired that the PD *Daisy*, punching home from Shetland grounds through a southerly gale had sprung a leak and despite the heroic efforts of the crew, she had finally sunk.

All hands were in a rubber liferaft, but before abandoning ship, skipper Jim Bruce had managed to send out a May Day signal with an approximate position.

Since the *Daisy's* wireless aerials had been torn away by stress of weather, it was something of a miracle that the May Day was heard at all, but it was picked up by another Peterhead boat only a few miles from her home port, and thus the news was relayed to the shore.

Now Peterhead was full of boats, but since they had been fishing in local waters, they had landed their catches in the morning and the crews had gone home, some to ports as far away as Buckie. Others had gone on picnics as I myself had intended; most had gone beyond immediate recall.

So the boats which left port on their search-and-rescue mission were manned by scratch crews, a motley throng of fishermen, landlubbers, towrags, warriedrags and swipins o' the pier. That afternoon not a single soul could be seen around the harbours.

On the *Silver Hope*, there were five of us; Tam, her skipper, Jim Mair, the singing fisherman, Colin, a school janitor, Neddy, a distillery worker and myself.

Apart from Tam, we were all incomers to the boat. Tam and Jim had been at sea all night so they required some sleep. This meant that for the first few hours I was in charge and boys was I sick!

Sea-sickness is a hellish affliction whose symptoms are as follows: the sense of smell is sharpened to an amazing degree; odours which would normally pass unnoticed assume the power to scunner a boddy; the lips develop a long-lost art of 'spittin' saxpences', then the mouth begins to produce prodigious amounts of saliva.

The entire body is inclined to shiver with cold then the stomach intimates that it wants to rebel against its contents, but somehow the contents do not wish to be evicted and the resultant conflict adversely affects the entire system.

Thus it was with me until I remembered the old-time

Herring drifters entering Yarmouth.

Last days of Sail and early days of Steam at Portknockie.

Tarring a new rope by hauling it through a trough of tar (Portknockie).

Boys of the Old Brigade take the sun on Buckpool pier which,
tho' built entirely without mortar, withstood all storms.

*Pairtin' the Mussels (St Combs). Each family had its own private 'scaap'
(mussel bed) on the rocky fore-shore where the tide kept the bait alive and fresh.*

*Memories are made of this. MB Twinkling Star (Skipper P. Buchan) 11th January, 1961.
Twelve lines of ninety hooks each. Bait — flusks (ink fish). Grounds — Buchan Deep.
Catch — 730 stone prime cod — value £411 (probably a record). Today? say £5,000.*

Built for sail, later motorised and now at the Fisheries Museum, Anstruther, 'Zulu' type fishing boat Research.

Forty-footers for the 4 o'clock sale at the Old Fishmarket, Peterhead, now a berth for grain boats.

June Rose *in her home port, berthed near the old Roundhouse where the whaling crews signed on.*

Fine to get a hurl even tho' the tyres are solid.

Herring gutters at work. Wearing gloves instead
of the normal 'cloots'.

The line skipper (my father) scans the distant horizon.
The barrels were for fish livers, perks for the crew.

The curer checks that his purchase is 'up to sample'. On the most trivial of excuses he would reject the catch then repurchase the same at a shilling per cran less!

A herring packer (Helen Duncan) ready to disappear into the barrel with yet another tier of herring.

A Real Family Affair!
Males, left to right — Skipper John Hugh Cowe, John Skinner (Balintore), David Cowe (skipper's brother),
A. Gowans (St Monance — brother-in-law), David and Jimmy Cowe, John Cowe and Willie Cowe (skipper's son).
Girls — Mary Bruce, Mary Cowe (top) and two Buckie girls.

fisherman's cure. Those interested please note. First, approach the skipper gently and ask for eighteen inches of twine. Next, approach the cook, not in your usual manner, but very respectfully and ask for a lump of fat from boiled beef, nice and blubbery.

Attach the twine to the fat, then swallow the fat whole, while keeping a firm grip on the twine. By means of the twine retrieve the fat. Repeat process if necessary.

I have never seen the physical process performed. The mental picture suffices to rid the system of unwelcome tenants and thereafter one begins to feel better. Slightly!

We were only a few miles off when we realised that there was no grub aboard! On a Saturday the lockers were empty and would not normally be replenished till Monday. Still, there were two stale loaves and an abundance of tay, so that would have to do.

When I informed Colin that he had been elected cook, he lifted his head half an inch of the deck and muttered: 'For God's sake Peter, gwaa' an' lat me dee in peace!'

When Tam and Jim were called for supper it was a mug of tea and a slice of bread and jam.

Still, we were a lot better off than the boys in the liferaft. Fancy sliding up and down these great watery hills, bracing themselves every time they heard an avalanche of broken sea coming!

When I thought of them I began to feel as if I were on the QE2.

When you see a fishing boat coming tearing towards the harbour entrance with a bone in her teeth you immediately think: 'By jings, she's fairly trampin'!' But, believe it or not, she'll not be doing more than 10 knots (say 11 m.p.h.).

So 140 miles was to take us 14 hours and, by that time, the raft could have drifted about 50 miles since she was launched! So that could be another five hours.

In the meantime, the skippers had 'gone into a huddle' on the radio and had elected a search commodore, Jimmy Watt of the *Aurora*. Thus the search would be organised instead of haphazard.

Jimmy had a rare crew; he had jumped aboard his boat and started the engine, then he had 'shanghaied' four fisher loons off the pier before setting sail. A fine baptism the loons got, awyte!

The leading searchers were ordered to slow down to let the stragglers catch up and, at break o' sky on the Sunday, the fleet, acting on instructions, formed a line twenty miles long, the individual boats being about a mile apart and all steering parallel courses.

I can only liken the fleet to the teeth of a giant rake looking for a pebble in a prairie. Each boat's crew would have half-a-mile on each side to scan, apart from a sharp look-out ahead, and everyone was exhorted to be on their toes.

It was not like searching a flat, calm sea with unlimited visibility. Na, na! There were times when the searchers could only see the tops of each other's masts so high was the swell, and it would have been easy to miss the raft without a conscientious look-out – which was in no wise lacking that day!

By this time, the search was international news and a few foreign vessels had joined in. Hour after hour the great 'rake' ploughed on, all twenty miles of it.

Then, towards mid-day, a great muckle Danish boat, which had joined the fleet near the centre and had been keeping pace with the Peterhead men, suddenly forged away ahead with superior speed and ran almost right on top of the raft.

Oh boys! What a sense of joy when we saw this ship rescue the castaways.

What did nationality matter? Absolutely nothing at all.

It was 'About ship' and 'Steer for home', and we sang all the way!

In vain did Stonehaven Radio appeal to us to desist! He could go and jump in the dock! Anxious listeners on the distant shore knew when they heard the singing that all was well, even when official confirmation had yet to come.

I think it was Alex Buchan (The Deevil) who had a chip shop on Seagate, that gave us a very touching version of 'Remember, child, your mother's prayer'.

In those days, we had no oil rigs with their helicopters to help – we could do the job in the only way we knew, and, thankfully, we were successful. We all got home early on Monday morning.

Finally, I would request Skipper Bruce, or any other skipper, that should he ever again contemplate taking to the liferaft – 'Please pick a bonny day, dee't a bittie nearer hame an' mak' sure it's nae a Setterday efterneen! Please!'

Guests for dinner

Once upon a time when the world was a far sweeter place, I had a classmate whose burning ambition was to earn good marks for writing a 'composition'.

Not until we reached a higher plane in our education did we hear the word 'essay'. Without fail our weekend homework was a composition on a subject of the teacher's choosing and many a weird and wonderful effort was offered up on a Monday morning. When the chosen subject was 'two things for which my home town is famous', Sammy, my pal, wrote that Peterhead was famous for its rain and its agricultural implements. Teacher was not impressed, and ordered Sammy to rewrite the whole script.

She would prefer something more sensible, and originality would bring extra marks. In his crest-fallen state, Sammy made a fatal mistake which he never repeated; he came to me for advice. 'Fit gart ye write aboot sic things?' says I. 'Weel, its aye rainin' an' Simpsons mak's cairts aside the Chucknie School!' was the reply.

Thereupon I gave him a lecture on the value of being original and factual at the same time. 'Ach t' pot,' says he. 'The Gut Factory and the Roon'hoose an' the Prison an' the Wine Waal an' the Buchanhaven Hotel (a crude open-air toilet on Buchanhaven Pier), that's a' been written aboot! Fit can I write aboot that's original?'

'Try the wifie wi' Fog an' Dogs Dirt,' says I. 'That'll be factual an' original tee.' The peer loon should ha'e kent better. Paraffin Kate gied 'im the strap!

But the same lad shook me next day when he defined 'gravity' as 'a little scarfie'. My govies, he got a penny fae the teacher for the lach she got! I could be factual and original, but I nivver got a penny!

On his fourteenth birthday Sammy left school for a job in a sawmill which stood on the site of the present telephone exchange. There he spent a 44-hour week 'jointing' staves for herring barrels, his reward being the princely sum of eight shillings and sixpence (42½p).

During Sammy's second year there his pay rose to ten bob (50p), but he took a proper scunner to the job and left it to join the Noble and Ancient Order of Drifter Cooks, not one of whose illustrious members was normal. Now, before you sue me for libel or dam me for sewages, let me give you a challenge!

Get yourself a steel tank 8 ft. 6 in. long, 7 ft. wide and 6 ft. high. In one end of the tank near the right-hand corner cut an arched doorway whose sill must be 10 in. high. Now in the far left-hand corner as you look in at the door, fix a big coal-burning stove and in the near left-hand corner fix a steel bunker 3 ft. high to hold two bags of coal.

Between the stove and the bunker sufficient space must be provided for the oven door to open downwards. Close to your left shoulder, from floor to roof, fix a wooden post about 10 in. thick to represent the mizzen mast and between that and the bunker rig a little shelf for a seat.

Now at the near end of the stove cut a hole in the floor (say 2 ft. square) to represent the hatchway to the cabin, not forgetting the guard rail to keep you from falling down the hole. The strip of floor in front of you is a passage and must not be otherwise used, so you are left with a floor approximately 5 ft. − 3 ft., the cook's domain. There is no sink and no running water because the water tank is bolted to the outside wall. The only light is from an acetylene gas jet.

Now choose any normal man you know, give him a set of pots and pans and a bucket, then put him into the steel tank with strict orders that for the next fortnight he must produce at least three square meals for ten men every day, not counting the fly-cups.

He'll be on his feet 20 hours daily. To make things realistic you'll have to set the tank on a machine which can produce the motions of the cake-walk, helter-skelter and roller-coaster all at the same time, and you must flood the place, frequently ankle-deep in sea water.

At the end of a fortnight of non-stop treatment, have a look at your normal man and, if he is still alive, he'll be a nervous wreck, pleading for mercy.

But not so the drifter cooks. They were not normal men – they were magicians who could teach Paul Daniels a thing or two. We hear aye aboot gallant skippers whose gallantry is usually commensurate with their success. We also hear about heroic deckies toiling on storm-swept decks.

Both skipper and deckie alike may have at home a loving wife who is busy keepin' his linner het while she is lashed to death wi' down quilts, but athoot the chiel in the galley the gallantry and heroics would fade and die.

The heart of the ship is the galley, not the wheelhouse. Noo fit aboot Sammy? Weel, Sammy wis cook in a drifter at Yarmouth far he'd gotten in tow wi' a Buckie quine. In a rash moment he had invited her to come doon for her denner on Sunday.

Oh aye, she wid come if her twa neepers could come an a'. So it was arranged that the three quines would be guests for Sunday lunch. Sammy was no mean cook! His culinary compositions were beyond belief altho' his literary compositions had been failures. Roast beef and Yorkshire pudding, followed by a wonderful trifle, then the inevitable cuppa. That was to be the menu.

Sammy saw to it that the cabin was spotless. 'For ony sake redd up that bed o' yours, it's like a horse's guts.' This to a young deckie.

But there was one problem – fresh milk. The quines widna like tinned milk in their tay and on board ship there was nothing else.

'Leave that to me,' says the skipper, who nipped across the pier to a shoppie far he bocht twa pints o' milk and persuaded the good lady to lend him a milk jug with a floral design.

Behold our Sammy then at the end of a first-class meal when the tea mugs were steaming hot. Behold him at the end of the crowded table wi' the bonny joog in his nieve and just listen as he says: 'Sugar yersels noo, quines, and I'll come roon' an' milk ye!'

Factual? Hardly! Original? Fit sorra idder! I telt ye he wisna normal!

Scalders and other hot stuff in beach pyjamas

When I was a barfit loon playing along the shore, it was quite common to find the beach thickly strewn with jellyfish of a semi-transparent bluish colour.

In diameter they varied from saucer to dinner plate dimensions; in consistency they were fairly firm and every one had four pink rings like eyes. We called them 'slivery doctors' and treated them with contempt. Hairmless breets!

But these were only distant relations of the hellish beasts which are the bane of the fisherman's life! Blue and white or red in colour with long, trailing tentacles, the fisherman's enemy is a mass of filthy rottenness, a scavenger of the sea. It doesn't rear up and bite you, but if ever you come across one, leave it severely alone.

It thrives in amazing numbers during the warm summer months and it seems to delight in rain and close, smuchty weather. English fishermen call these beasties 'unprintable' jellies; Sooth-kintra Scots call them 'slithers' but the fishers of the north-east call them 'scalders', and a more appropriate name would be hard to find.

They cannot mesh in a net; they would simply disintegrate. But they slide down a herring net when the net is being hauled and they leave particles of filthy slime along the nets' entire length. In the hauling process, which is 'haul-an'-shak', to shake the herrings out, drops of water fly all over the place, carrying particles of poisonous jelly which attack any face which may be handy.

The effects may or may not be immediate, depending on the texture of the victim's skin, but stand by when you get into the warmth of your bunk! Fire will torment you where the skin is tender, round the eyes, nostrils and mouth and especially between the fingers. It's like the awful smarting sensation you get when you've put your hand into 'ower het watter', but it doesn't go away!

I have seen men really frantic with the torture. The medical profession may have an antidote in these enlightened days but twenty-odd years ago there was none. It has been known for a crew to refuse duty when the 'scalders' were really thick!

They would leave the nets till daylight in the hope that the beasts would submerge as the sun rose. This didn't always work! One reasonably effective protection was the nylon stocking pulled over the head but it was strange indeed to see a crew of masked thugs hauling herring nets!

Trawlermen and seine-net men do not suffer to the same extent but it is quite common for the tail of a flapping cod to send a splat of jelly into a body's face. Some folk swear that the blues are worst, others swear by the reds, most swear at them both.

The biggest scalders I have ever seen were in the Irish Sea, and boys, they were bobby dazzlers! The year? Say 1933? The hit song was 'Auf Wiedersehen' and beach pyjamas had just appeared on the scene. What bold shameless women they were to wear nothing but 'a jacketie an' a pair o' breekies'. So said some of the letters to the editor!

When we were in any of the Manx ports bevies of beach-pyjamaed girls thronged the quay to watch the fishing boats. We simply loved it when a shower of rain sent the girls running for shelter. Then it was obvious that there were more jellies on the quay than in the whole Irish Sea! Did I look the other way? That'll be the day!

Our base that summer was Ardglass in Co. Down. I can remember our surprise at the extreme age of some of the 'girls' who gutted the herrings on the quay. They really were 'aul' wifies', who spoke Irish Gaelic.

There we met fishermen from Southern Ireland; quiet, decent men they were, but their boats and gear were no great shakes. Where we had canvas buoys, which we called 'bowse', these Irishmen used the bladders from farm animals.

The mouth of the bladder was lashed tightly round a cotton reel (pirn), so that the float could be inflated by blowing through the hole in the pirn which could be easily plugged. The inflated bladder was then sheathed in netting which in turn could be tied to the herring net. In Scotland this primitive method had died out fifty years before.

The staple diet of these Irishmen was contained in a great muckle broth pot wherein a 'hale ham was boiled with cabbages and peas. Only at weekends did their diet vary and the broth pot was replenished on Mondays.

Doubtless these Irish fishers like their Scots brothers have come a long way since those days. The beach-pyjama girls would be 'foosty aul' fizzers' nowadays and I'm thinkin' that the total attire of a modern beach girl would be richt handy for liftin' a het broth-pot.

But ye may be sure the scalders are aye the same!

Bounty in the fog

Visitors to the seaside must be short-sighted indeed if they fail to notice that, at certain times, the sea comes a tremendous distance up the beach, while at other times, it recedes an equally tremendous distance, leaving a great expanse of firm, wet sand exposed to view. 'Aha!' they say. 'The tide's in,' or 'the tide's out', depending on the amount of beach which is available for use.

Message boys delivering stores to fishing boats like to do the job when they can simply step off the pier on to the boat wi' their bags o' tatties, etc. If they are obliged to make their deliveries when the tide's out, they find the shippies 'hine doon', so they have to lower their goods on ropes or clamber with them down dirty ladders.

So the tide comes in, then goes out again; it rises and falls. Ah! you knew all this before, did you? Well, it is possible, that you are ignorant of the fact that the tide also flows like a river and a pretty smart river at that!

Without trying to be technical about it, let me inform you that the tide originates away in the belly of the ocean somewhere about the Sargasso Sea or some other God-forsaken place. It is a great surge of water, quite incomprehensible in its magnitude, which makes its way towards the British Isles and many other places besides.

Up the West Coast it comes, round Cape Wrath towards the Orkneys where it roars through the Pentland and Westray Firths like a wild beast, before changing course for Rattray Head.

On the way it fills all the harbours and the lochs, it fills the Moray Firth and its offshoots. In fact, it fills the whole North Sea! That's the flood tide, the tide comin' in!

For six hours it runs thus, then it pauses a wee while for breath. That pause is called slack water or 'the slack', then the tide turns and runs all the way back again, only this time it sucks all the water out of the Firths and lochs and bays; that is the ebb tide, the tide going out! That is merely a rough sketch of what is meant by 'tide', and it may help you to understand my tale.

The powers-that-be make regular studies of the direction and strength of the tidal streams around the British Isles and it is quite simple to obtain a copy of their charts. They may use several methods of measurement, of which I am completely ignorant, but I am well versed in one method which they use, and this is the use of a 'floating body'.

If you drop a floating body into the sea in an accurately plotted position and recover it later in another accurately plotted position it should be possible to measure the drift.

Now, about thirty years ago, there appeared in most of the salesmen's offices a notice to the effect that several of these floating bodies were to be released in the North Sea. Any skipper finding one should bring the same to the nearest Fishery Office, the appropriate time and position duly noted. Then he would get five bob! A very generous institution indeed, the Fishery Office.

Picture now the Peterhead fishing fleet, proceeding to sea on a foggy afternoon in search of the silver darlin's. It wasn't exactly as thick as guts but still thick enough to necessitate a keen look-out. I should explain here that fishermen usually describe fog as 'thickness'.

Our course was east-by-south, three-quarter speed and we were about ten miles from the shore when one of the deckies yelled: 'Hey, that's een o' yon things that's worth five bob!' We had it aboard in a tick then resumed our course after noting the time and the exact position as recorded by the Decca Navigator.

Then a wee while later, we found another and yet another. At five bob a time we were doing quite nicely. It was only when we had half a dozen on board that I noticed that these valuable finds were exactly a mile apart, and certain niggling doubts assailed me, but there was no denying the young deckies who greeted each new find with delight.

The fifteenth body had just been recovered when the fog lifted, and there, dead ahead of us, was a Fishery boat actually planting the things in the sea! All unknown to him we had been following in his wake picking up the bounty.

What to do now? We could hardly claim payment for that which hadn't been five minutes in the water! We could have contacted the Fishery boat and given him back his 'bodies' but to save the good man (and myself) a lot of embarrassment we overtook him at full speed and at such a distance that he couldn't see what we had on our deck. Then, about three miles dead ahead of him we consigned the lot to the deep, where he couldn't fail to find them.

As we sailed away, leaving the little flaggies fluttering gaily in the light breeze, I heard one of the deckies remark: 'I'll bet that'll shak' 'is cotton drawers!'

So, if you ever read that the tidal streams in the North Sea gather all floating objects together, to dump them in a heap off Peterhead, you'll know that the information is incorrect.

Hunting in the dark for paaps!

From Buchan Ness to Harcla Head, just south of Collieston, the Buchan coast is one long stretch of precipitous cliff, broken only by the beautiful golden beach at Cruden Bay.

The word 'Cruden' is very ancient and means 'the killing of the Danes', so there must have been a great battle in these quarters long ago. But local fishermen never use the term Cruden Bay.

For them it is the Ward Bay; the rocky headland at the north end of the bay is the Ward Head, and the little fishing village of Port Errol is 'the Ward', whose inhabitants are thus 'Wardies'.

The Wardies had a harbour of which they were extremely proud. It was ideal for yawls of up to 25 ft. and the fact that the harbour was practically dry at low-water did not in any way lessen the Wardies' pride. At least they didn't have to draw their boats up on a beach as some folk did! These Wardies were industrious line fishermen but with the advent of the seine net they forsook the haddock line, with its attendant labours, for the new art of seining for 'plashies' (plaice).

Still, the winter months found them back at their lug lines fishing for codlings as far south as Neebra Water (the Ythan estuary). The entrance to the main basin of the harbour could be sealed off in extreme weather by huge wooden booms which were lowered into slots in the pier by means of a hand-powered crane.

It's not all that long ago, surely, since the Wardies got a set of booms from Peterhead, second-hand, but nonetheless ideal once they were shortened to fit the narrow channel. Over the last 40 years the harbour has silted up to a marked degree, but recent efforts by loyal small-boat enthusiasts have remedied this. The piers, however, are in a sorry state which would be very costly to put right.

The Wardies, before they became extinct, bore names such as Summers, Milne, Robertson, Masson and Tait. Once I asked a Wardie friend whose name was John Robertson (Gorlan's Jock) – 'Is there nae Buchans in this place, Jock?' To which he replied 'Peter!' If the Buchans wis to come here we wid ha'e t' flit!'

'Far wid ye ging?' says I.

'We wid ging an' bide wi' the Cannlies!' says he.

'An' fa on earth's the Cannlies?'

'The Faulers! The Finnyfaul men! They hiv candle lanterns so we ca' them the Cannlies.'

'An' fit div they use the cannle lanterns for?'

'Oh! says Jock, 'They ging oot in the dark lookin' for paaps!'

'Good grief!' says I. 'I nivver thocht the Faulers wis folk like that! The kitchie deems on the fairms wid need to ha'e their doors lockit!'

'Ach! Ye ken that's nae fit I mean,' laughed Jock. 'It's bait they're lookin' for!'

Fine did I ken fit he meant. The paap (note the long vowel) is a sea creature which clings to the rocks in places where man cannot reach it except at low-water on an extremely big tide. No doubt it has a Latin name as lang as Leith Walk, but fishermen are notoriously poor at Latin.

The paap is about the size of a sma' tattie and has a consistency resembling a stiff jube-jube. It can vary in colour from red to orange and it makes the finest bait you ever saw. Cod find it irresistible.

One really outstanding feature about this beastie is that it can be used over and over again, especially if you sprinkle brown sugar over it! I'm giving away trade secrets now so I'll ha'e to watch mysel'! Dinna say that I tellt ye!

Since low-water with a big ebb is around 8 or 9 p.m. (in this airt), you can see the need for the cannle lanterns.

Whinnyfold or Finnyfaul (hence the name 'Faulers') is a tiny hamlet which sits on top of the cliff at the south end of Cruden Bay. I have a suspicion that the folks who built the houses there had a recipe for some powerful adhesive which stuck the hooses to their foonds, otherwise they would have been blown into the sea.

There is at Finnyfaul no harbour, only an open shore from which the boaties had to be launched daily and whereon they had to be drawn up nightly. The only access to this shore is by means of a precipitous footpath and generations of Finnyfaul women struggled up this path with creels of fish on their backs. Every mortal thing had to be transported via this route and it must have been slave labour indeed. After many weary years of toil, somebody thought of installing a 'Blondin' from the cliff-top to the shore. This was a wire cable on which ran a pulley, and goods suspended from this pulley could be pulled up from the beach. It was indeed a great labour-saving device, but it had been in use for only a few years when the fisher population of the hamlet ceased to be.

The shore at Finhyfaul was used by sma' boaties only. It lies just a castie on the south side of that dreaded reef, the Skares. A short distance north of this shore there is another cove called The Breythaven (Broadhaven) and it was here that the Faulers drew up their bigger herrin' boats when the season decreed.

Finnyfaul has produced a race of sterling fishermen whose descendants are now mostly in Peterhead. They were Morgans, Formans, Hays and Caies. Once I asked a good friend of mine, Jocky Morgan —

'Is there nae Buchans here, Jock?'

'Peter!' says he, 'if the Buchans wis to come here we wid ha'e to flit!'

'Far wid ye ging?' says I.

'Och, we wid ging an' bide wi' the Hoolits!'

'Fa on earth's the Hoolits?'

'Yon mob that bides in the Ward! They're for ivver fartin' aboot in the dark athoot a licht! An' there's never a licht on their boats! They're jist nae mowse! I think they can see in the dark!'

'Wid they ging oot lookin' for paaps in the dark, Jock?'

'Aye! I'm sure they wid' he exclaimed. 'The Hoolits is fit for onything!' Then seeing the twinkle in my eye he gave me a playful cuff on the ear. 'Away ye go, ye coorse tink!'

But it is a fact that, one wild morning in the days of sail, the whole Cannlie population stood in awe on the cliff-top watching a boat coming from the southward. The wind was storm-force southerly and the tide was in full flood, creating, at the outer point of the Skares reef, conditions of such awful ferocity that the boat could not possibly survive. Of this the watchers were certain, for they knew the Skares! And still the vessel stood on, heading for disaster.

But her skipper knew the Skares like the back of his hand, so, instead of tackling the maelstrom at the outside, he took his vessel, under full sail, through the narrow, tortuous channel which lies between the inner edge of the reef and the cliff. There the tide had shot its bolt and the sea was much calmer. Many of the cliff-top throng turned their backs as this gallant skipper tackled the impossible.

Only those who know this channel (and there are not many) can judge how daring the feat was. It was seamanship at its highest pinnacle and it succeeded. The boat came safely through.

The skipper was 'Een o' yon mob that bides in the Ward' – A Hoolit! And his name was Milne!

So the Cannlies didn't have a monopoly on seamen.

But, sadly, Fauler or Cannlie, Wardie or Hoolit, they are no longer with us and the world is the poorer for their passing.

Ripping yarns of the Arctic

Every vessel which enters Peterhead harbour passes a short stone jetty called the Blubber Box, a name from the days when the whalers landed their blubber there.

At the head of the jetty was the Boil-yard, where the blubber was boiled; the site is now an oil depot. Towards the end of the last century the Blue Toon had such a sizeable fleet of whaling ships that the local *Sentinel* could publish a list of the names of the ships which would sail that particular week.

The fair city of Dundee also had whalers and the Dundee paper used to say: 'Half of the whaling fleet sailed today; the other half will sail next week.' There were only two ships in the Dundee fleet! A touch of professional jealousy maybe.

The actual whaling fleet had disappeared many years before I was born, but I can well remember climbing the rigging of the *Rosie*, an old whaler which had lain dormant in Peterhead for years and I can clearly remember the day she sailed for the Arctic all decked out with bunting.

Mair than half the toon thronged the quay that day and many a head shook in sheer disbelief that a ship should sail on Sunday. 'Nae gweed wid come o' that!'

The Peterhead whalers called the Eskimos 'Yakkies' from the real name 'Yaqui', and I can clearly recall the time when a Yakkie loon spent a holiday in the Blue Toon. The peer loon couldna' stan' the Peterheid wither ava! Bugs and germs he had never met before attacked him with gusto so that 'he nivver had a weel day'. So he was sent home to the Arctic where he recovered completely and lived to a ripe old age.

The last survivors of the whaling race were old, old men when I was a littlin and the few who were still able to work were cooks in the drifters. Decrepit they may have been but boys-a-boys they could fairly spin a yarn!

Every blessed one of them had had at least one face-to-face encounter (an 'eyeball') with a Polar Bear! 'It's the best cure for constipation ye ever saw, my loon!' There must have been a Polar Bear behind every ice-hummock.

Life on the whalers must have been very hard indeed. When a whale was sighted the ship's boats were lowered and their crews would endeavour to row close to the whale so that a marksman in the bow could ram a harpoon into the unsuspecting monster.

Attached to the harpoon there was a line about 200 fathoms in length with a barrel on the end of it. When the wounded whale sounded (dived) the line would go hissing over the boatie's rail until the barrel had to go overboard as well, but since the whale must come to the surface to breathe, the oarsmen could usually keep track of the barrel and having retrieved it, the seamen would 'play their fish'.

Many boats and men were lost in this perilous game for an enraged whale is not a 25 lb. salmon. It was a case of wearing the monster down. 'Gie her line' or 'Take up the slack' were the orders as the occasion required. I widna fancy being towed in an open boat by a thirty ton monster, especially if there were ice floes around!

These rowing cutters, all built in the Blue Toon, were sturdy craft. To this very day the fishermen along the coasts of Baffin Land and Greenland have what they call 'Peterhead boats', faithful replicas of the whalers' boats.

Scarcely a year passed without some ship or another being frozen in among the pack ice. Then the crew would abandon ship and bide in igloos along wi' the Yakkies! Since the natives were very hospitable and since there were quite a few females around, ye could get a 'bidie-in' for the winter, 'nae bother ava'!

But the Eskimo belles had a delectable custom of washing their hair in urine to make their tresses glossy and healthy, so the Blue Mogganers didn't have a bed of roses! Oh gyaad! I'm thankfu' gled my missus disna dip her heid in the po!

The whalers were not classed as fisher folk altho' they lived among the fishers and often married fisher quines. They signed on Articles and got a fixed wage plus a bonus if the season's catch was good. This was something foreign to fisher folk who had to accept the maxim 'No fish – no money', and forbye the whalers had different ranks such as ordinary seamen, A.B., bosun, harpooner, ship's carpenter, etc.

One crack harpooner was a man whom we'll call Robbie. His hoosie was a but-an'-ben wi' a little closetie in the middle. There was no provision whatsoever for sanitation, not even an outside toilet.

In this respect Robbie's hoosie was no different from the others in the fisher villages. Any boys in the family were expected to seek a secluded spot among the rocks when answering the call of nature; for other members of the household there was a pail which was 'teemed' every morning where the tide would exert its twice-daily purge. This is fact, not fiction. Thousands of houses in Scotland had no toilets until some thirty years ago!

I have very clear memories of living in spotlessly clean two-storey houses on the West Coast and in the Hebrides where the only loo was the byre. Aye! As late as the 1950s too!

Well, now, Robbie was seated at his fireside in the glow of the paraffin lamp along with his better half, Meg. Between them, on the fender-stool the cat basked in the heat of the open fire.

While Meg busied herself darning Robbie's socks, he gave her an account of the harpooning and eventual despatch of a whale, but Meg was rather green in nautical matters and didn't seem to understand very clearly. So Robbie, in exasperation, decided that an object lesson was required.

'Hud ee this ball o' worsit,' says he to Meg as he threaded the end into a darning needle. Then, taking very careful aim he 'harpooned' the cat which took sheet oot the door like an evil speerit while Robbie yelled 'Gie 'er line, Meg, gie 'er line!'

When the worsit stoppit rinnin' oot, the order was 'Tak' in the slack noo, Meg: ye've lost the brute!'

Gweed forgi'e me for thinkin' sometimes that the aul' whaler that tellt me that story wis just a born leear!

Foolin' the Board o' Trade

The gadgetry on a modern fishing boat is something to behold! Electronic devices of all kinds occupy most of the wheelhouse space and since most of the devices are in duplicate the place resembles a power station.

Navigational and fishing aids are largely 'on hire' and several firms have agents in all the major ports to service their products. These agents are on call 24 hours a day, seven days a week so a fishing skipper can call on their services at any time.

The safety devices on the boats are really excellent and rightly so. These are the responsibility of the boat-owners and must be kept up to the mark – the Board of Trade sees to that! I have heard skippers complaining bitterly that first-class gear has been condemned when less than a year old, regardless of the fact that it has been unused and was the best obtainable when purchased.

The reason given – 'out of date now'! It can cost a lot of money to keep up to date when inspections are so rigorous.

When I was at sea, however, things were vastly different. There were of course certain requirements which were mandatory, but once the apparatus was there it could lie neglected for years, so that in an emergency it often proved useless. Things were left largely to the conscience of individual owners so in many cases maintenance was poor and supervision lax.

I once heard of an Aberdeen trawler – you know the type – old and battered and more or less devoid of paint. Well now, this shippie was towing her trawl in the North Sea when it fouled an obstruction on the seabed. In fishermen's parlance such an obstruction is 'a fastener'.

The skipper (Rascal Dan) was a man who had through years of bitter experience, gained a remarkable degree of skill in the art of recovering gear from fasteners, but apparently this was the daddy of them all. After many hours of fruitless endeavour, with wire ropes twanging like fiddle-strings and bad words fleein' like sparks, Dan was almost ready to give up and chop the whole lot away when the mate reported that 'fitever this thing is, it seems to be aff the boddim noo'!

This gave Dan fresh heart and inch by inch the fastener was brought to the surface where, lo and behold, it turned out to be a trawler, complete in every detail.

She had been lost in a storm some fifty years before. Now to cut a long story short, Dan and his crew boarded their 'find' and scuttled their own ship. As Dan said later, 'It wid ha'e been a shame t' dee onything else! She wis sic an afa lot better'! True or false? Please yersel'!

I recall a certain morning in a chandlery in Peterhead when I picked up a brass object from the counter and started to play idly with it. 'For ony sake lay that thing doon,' said the storekeeper. 'A'body that comes in fichers wi' that, an' some lads thumps the coonter wi't fin they're argyin'!'

'A'richt!' says I, 'Fit is't onywye?'

'It's a spray nozzle for the hose! Accordin' t' the Boord o' Trade ye're supposed to' ha'e een o' them! Ye'll get it for half-price if ye'll tak' it oot o' my sicht!'

I took it to the boat and put it in the breist o' my bed along wi' the ither odds an' sods that made my bed so lumpy.

Well, one day that winter we were lying at the pier in Shields with six Duffers (Macduff boats) on our off-side. We would all have been at sea had the weather been good.

Suddenly there appeared on the scene a Boord o' Trade mannie on a tour of inspection. Now some of these mannies had a bee in their bonnet about lifebuoys; with others it was lights, or pumps or something else. Well, this mannie started in our focsle and went through the whole boat, missing nothing out.

Finally he came to me and said: 'You keep a remarkably tidy boat, skip, but I fail to see your spray nozzle!'

'Och!' says I, 'It's in the breist o' my bed! I'll get it!'

'That's a most peculiar place to keep it! says he. 'It's supposed to be in the hose; for fire-fighting, you know!'

'Fine div I ken that!' says I 'But ye canna wash fish wi' a spray nozzle an' to leave it aboot the deck wid be an open invitation to thiefs! It's solid braiss, ye ken!'

He hummed an' hawed a fylie then he says, 'OK skip,

carry on! But without that nozzle you would not have been allowed to sail!'

So this was the bee in this lad's bonnet. Spray nozzles for hoses! After jotting a few notes in his bookie he boarded our next door neighbour, the *Zephyr* of Macduff and, as before, he started in the focsle.

'Foo did 'ee get on Peter?' says Walter, her skipper.

'A'richt!' says I. 'Ye see, we hiv a spray nozzle!'

'A fit did ye say? Nivver heard that een afore! Fit neist?'

'Weel!' says I, 'It's time ye got een or ye winna get t' the sea!'

'Far can I get sic a thing at this time o' day! The mannie's aboord noo. Eh! sirss, sirss!'

'Ha'e! says I, 'Stick that in the breist o' yer bed, Walter!' So Walter got our nozzle on loan with a briefing on how to answer the mannie.

The end result was that seven boats (our tier) were at sea next morning while the others were delayed pending the arrival of spray nozzles from Newcastle.

The mannie must have thought that the Scotties were most peculiar folk. 'Every one of them that has a spray nozzle keeps it in his bunk!'

I could ha'e tellt 'im something queerer than that! Ivvery blessed wan o' them got a gweed shot neist day, but deil the sowl said 'Boo' for the len' o' my nozzle!

I'm tellin' ye! The Jews is nae a' in Jerusalem!

Horse of a different colour

'Twas late in the summer of 1945 and the sea was like glass, smoked glass gleaming in the light of the half-risen sun. In our 40-foot boatie we were hauling our seine net at the conclusion of our first haul of the day and it was quite obvious that the net was well filled with fish.

Hordes of screaming gulls were circling the floating bag; some were even standing on it, and solan geese were diving from a great height to catch the small fry which had slipped through the meshes.

Of course we were all pleasantly excited but our pleasure was tinged with alarm, for there was a great muckle ship heading straight towards us. Did he see us? Did he not? If he did see us it was time he was altering course otherwise we would be sliced in two! If we tried to tow the net out of his path we would probably go the wrong way and no doubt we would burst the net.

Ah! Keep the heid lads, he's altering now and apparently he's slowing down. The great bow-wave from the approaching vessel died away and she came to a stop about 20 yards away just as we got the bag aboard.

Oh, what a bonny ship she was! One of the very latest trawlers from Hull, she had been released from naval service and returned to her owners. Even in their wartime camouflage such ships were bonny craft but here was one in her company colours, spick and span from stem to stern, a joy to behold.

'Apologies if I scared the life out of you, lads! I was watching you all the time. Could we have a fry, please?'

Now, fancy a great ocean-going trawler seekin' a fry fae a yole! Oh aye! He wid get a fry! Fit was he seekin'?

'A basket of haddock and a basket of sprags (codlings).'

As we passed the fish across we noticed that every one of the crew was clad in new gear. Just home from the Navy! Bound for the White Sea. First trip ever for the ship. Every man sick of the sight of Spam and beans-on-toast and tinned sausages; dying to taste fresh fish! And it would be a few days yet before they caught any of their own, for the White Sea was a long way off!

It was most unusual to see such a ship only three miles from Buchan Ness, but for a long time after the war vessels bound for distant grounds had to stick to explicit routes until certain minefields had been swept.

Oh aye, ye could get a fry and we wanted no payment from fellow fishermen but he insisted that we accept a bottle of Johnnie Walker and a carton of fags. 'Cheerio boys, all the best! Call again any time!' And he was on his way, no more than 26 years of age I'd say. Very young for a skipper of such a ship!

Well, the fags didn't last long but the bottle lay untouched in a locker for at least a year, then it was stolen. We didna drink it? No! We had not the slightest interest in it!

Most of the fishermen of my generation were teetotal. Of course there were those who imbibed rather freely, but they were in the minority. And then there were those quiet, decent lads whose only vice was a liking for a quiet pint on a Setterday nicht.

Such were two pals from one of the villages which lie between the Broch and Rattray Head. Since these villages had no licensed premises our heroes had to make a journey of five or six miles to a certain hostelry which stands on the Peterhead-Broch road. Neither of the pair had even heard of a motor car; cars were still a year or two in the future, so they simply followed their normal routine.

Behold then our two stalwarts hiring a horse and gig to convey them to the inn. Nothing unusual about that in those days, and the horsie would take them safely home should they over-indulge, which was not at all likely. On arrival at their desired haven Jock, the younger of the pair, hitched the horsie to the rail, remarking as he did so that she widna need a starn-rope.

After a very pleasant evening in the company of some country folk the two mariners set out on the homeward trip. Then in the deep dusk of late summer, just as Fiddler's Green was close on their starboard beam Jock gied Daavit a richt dunt in the ribs.

'Hey, Daavit! We're awa' wi' the wrang horse!'

'Dinna be daft, Jock. This is the horse we left hame wi'.'

''Tis nott!' says Jock. ''Tis sott!' says Daavit.

'I'm tellin' ye this is nae the horse we left hame wi',' says Jock patiently.

'Weel noo!' replies Daavit, 'Ye may ken aboot boats an' gear an' fish, but I canna see fit wye the likes o' you can possibly ken aboot a horse. Fut gar ye think this is nae oor horsie?'

'Aha!' says Jock. 'This horsie piddles ower the starn; oor horsie piddled amidships!'

An' he wis richt!

Jeemsie lands the Turk in hot custard

Duncan Elrick was not quite unique but he was certainly most unusual in that he was a country chiel that made his living at the sea.

Born and 'fessen up' on the small holding of Poverty-knap (pronounce the 'K'), somewye atween the Prop o' Ythsie an' the Myre o' Bedlam, he had serred his time wi' the Cooncil amon' traction engines and steam wagons, but a desire for adventure had led him to the sea where he had obtained and held for five years the post of chief engineer on the good ship *Meadowsweet*, one of the Peterhead herring drifters.

The *Meadowsweet's* skipper was Bob McTurk, known all around the coast as 'The Turk' and he had sic a bummer o' a belly that, for a while, Jeemsie the cook thocht the skipper had a washin'-hoose biler up his ganjie. Mair aboot that later, maybe!

Well now, Duncan had been hame for the weekend bidin' wi's brither an' gweed-sister an' their twa loons. To his young nephews Uncle Dunk was a knight in shining armour! Didn't he have to face mountainous seas and fearsome tempests at Cape Horn to get this bonny fry o' herrin' for their supper? Weel awyte, that an' mair, for he had to keep a constant watch for the cannibals who put out their dug-out canoes from the Bullers o' Buchan to prey upon unsuspecting fishers!

In fact, the verra day o' the Turra Show, a great muckle sea monster had seized the *Meadowsweet* in its gaping jaws, and only Duncan's presence of mind had saved the day, for he had shovelled red-hot fire from the boiler down the monster's throat!

'Wis she bigger nor a coo, Uncle Dunk?'

'Bigger nor a coo? I'm tellin' ye, fin I wis lookin' doon her throat I saw three stirks in her stammick!'

'Fresians or Herefords Uncle Dunk?'

'I couldna see them richt for aa the steam!'

Wasn't 'at a shame that their uncle's name was never in the *P & J*. He would get a medal someday. Surely!

Little did they ken that while they were fast asleep Duncan wis awa' wi' Hilly's kitchie deem.

Monday morning saw Duncan step aboard the *Meadowsweet*. There was no real need for Duncan to arrive early for the fireman had everything under control and in any case the ship wouldn't sail till afternoon.

In one hand Duncan had a bag containing twa dizzen chippit eggs while in the opposite oxter he carried an enormous bunch o' rhubarb, a present fae his gweed-sister who had said: 'If the fishers di'sna want it, it'll be handy for chokin' the neist monster ye meet!'

Jeemsie, the cook, Duncan's bosom pal eyed the rhubarb with some concern. 'Fit div ye dee wi' that, Duncan? My mither nivver learnt me onything aboot rhubarb!'

'Och! ye chap it into bitties and stew't, an' it's better if ye hiv a suppie custard along wi't. Hiv ye ony custard in the press?'

'It's nae a press! It's a locker, Duncan, an' there's nae custard in't. There's plenty semolina an' birdies eenies (sago) but nae custard. Still we'll seen sort that! I'll get some fae the grocer. Foo muckle will I get?'

'For ten men ye'll need a gweed sup, Jeemsie!'

In the afternoon, as soon as the shippie had cleared the port, most of the crew turned in leaving a responsible man at the wheel and Duncan to fire the boiler. As his duties allowed he would help Jeemsie to prepare an exotic meal for the crew.

'We'll pit the chappit rhubarb in the tattie-pot an' let it sooss awa' for an 'oor or twa! says he. 'Meantime we'll sort the custard an' I think we'll use the broth pot for that.'

'Did yer mither learn ye aboot custard Duncan?' says Jeemsie.

'No, she didna. I dinna ken muckle aboot it.'

'Weel, that mak's twa o's, but we'll ha'e a go at it!' says the cook.

Soon the custard was ready and pronounced first-class but then our heroes were faced with the problem of over-production.

'Far are we gaun t' pit the stuff? says Jeemsie. 'There's nae a pudden dish in Scotland could hud the half o't. Well aa ha'e sair airms afore we get this lot suppit!'

Duncan was silent, realising he had miscalculated. Then in a flash of inspiration he cried 'Fit aboot yon great muckle "nammle" basin that ye eesed t' ha'e?'

'The verra dunt!' says Jeemsie, 'I'll get it'!

As a beginner Jeemsie had not known the golden rule, 'One hand for the ship and the other for yourself', but he had soon learned that a basin required both hands, leaving him helpless when negotiating the cabin ladder. So the basin had been discarded for the superior bucket but now in this hour of need the basin would be invaluable.

'Far can we pit the thing for safety? says he, surveying the brimming basin. 'If we pit it ootside it'll be blaadit wi' sitt fae the funnel, an' it canna bide here in the galley!'

'Och! We'll pit it doon the stair,' says Duncan, again betraying his country origin. 'There's plenty o' room doon there!'

So now we find Duncan on his knees on the galley floor, handing the great basin o' pudden doon the trap to Jeemsie who stood in the cabin ready to receive it.

'There's a great sup left in the pot yet!' says the chief, 'Hiv ye nae anither dish my loon? I suppose a chunty pot wid be better than naething!'

Almost helpless with laughter Jeemsie laid the basin on the seat locker close to his own bunk where nobody would disturb it, but he forgot that in the upper bunk the ponderous bulk of the Turk lay sleeping.

Well, it had to happen! Some sixth sense had told the Turk that something was afoot so he climbed out of his bunk and promptly sat in the basin of hot custard. His fearsome roar brought to view several startled faces which were immediately assailed by great skirps o' fleein' pudden! Oh what a kirn! Siccan a sotter! It wis hingin' fae the deck, it wis plaistered ower the clock, it wis aa ower the place!

Nelson, the one-eyed deckie, was heard to remark that 'Yon wis the biggest splash I've seen since Andra Baird's horse fell into the hairber, an' that wis some splash!'

When the dreeps had settled and the furore had died down our two heroes had to buckle to with buckets and brushes and cloots to clean up the cabin.

As the discomfited pair crouched below the table, Jeemsie whispers to his pal, 'The skipper's reid mad the day, freen'.

'Aye! Fairly that!' says Duncan, 'But ye could easy cheer 'im up, I think!'

'Foo on earth could I dee that, noo?'

'Ging up an' speir if he wid like a clean hippen,' was the reply.

Driven clean round the bend!

Visitors to the Moray Firth coast are usually favourably impressed with the spick-and-span appearance of the houses of the fisher folk.

The immaculate paintwork on both wood and stone is positive proof that a great deal of work and not a little money have been lavished on these dwellings, which altho' they are not of granite are nevertheless soundly constructed to endure the rigours of the north-east climate.

There is something about these houses which reflects the nature of their owners, the pride of ownership.

This is not the arrogant pride of bigsiness or conceit but a softer, milder pride in such things as heritage and birthplace.

Where such things are concerned the fisher folk are a proud people indeed, but I must confess that I have never yet met any of them who spent any sleepless nights trying to decide whether they would be born 'fisher' or 'country'.

This same pride can be seen, albeit in a lesser form, in the boats, especially in the boats registered under the letters BCK (Buckie).

Seldom will you see a BCK boat in an orra state. Nae fears! The BCK lads are on the whole 'verra parteeclar' with their craft.

The letters BCK embrace that part of the coast which stretches from Portknockie (The Land o' Promise) in the east, to Port Gordon in the west, but Buckie is the port of registry.

Peterhead men, in their profound ignorance are inclined to class all BCK boats as 'Buckiemen', a title which many a skipper would resent.

It is quite common to see a BCK boat with her proper home port's name on the stern e.g. Portknockie, Portessie, Portgordon. There's a flash of the pride of birthplace and a strong hint of independence.

In the heyday of the drifters, the BCKs were a 'speak'. They were renowned for their immaculate appearance. The drifters built by Alex Hall, of Aberdeen, were probably the bonniest shippies afloat and to see one of them with the BCK registration was to see a picture of perfection.

I am thinking now of a particular Saturday afternoon in Yarmouth in 1946, when just under 1,000 drifters thronged the river. Scores of powerful steam-driven donkey pumps were in action as the boats were being washed down for the weekend. Herring scales by the million were dislodged from all deckwork and skited into the river.

I was busily engaged in this task when I noticed the beautiful, spotless state of our next door neighbour, a BCK.

She was like a model, so clean was she! The wheelhouse windows were so clean that they glistened in the autumn sun and a boy who was, to my expert eye, a first-year loon, was busy with the hose meticulously cleaning the decks.

He must have noticed my admiring glances for he cleared his throat and remarked 'You Peterheid men's nae verra parteeclar!'

'Fit gars ye think 'at my loon?' says I rather taken aback.

'Weel!' says he, 'ye're leavin' a lot o' scales on the windaes. Yer skipper winna see through them on Monday!'

I was silent for a moment, then he renewed his attack.

'That ship o' yours minds me on a wife wi' fool stockens, her masts is nae painted!'

I did my best to wither him with the sort of glance that an old man of thirty is entitled to throw at a mere stripling, but it was without effect so I decided that the best form of defence was attack!

'Peterheid men disna fash themsel's ower muckle aboot scales,' says I, 'but they're gey parteeclar aboot hygiene!'

'Fit div ye mean by hygiene?' says the loon.

'Hiv ye washed oot the water closet the day?' I queried.

'Och aye, it's gotten a richt sweel oot wi' the hose!'

Now the shippie he was on was an 'iron standard boat' i.e. she had been built by the government during World

94

War I, therefore she had a toilet, something rather uncommon in the fishing boats of those days.

Only 'standard boats' had toilets and the toilet was always on the port side of the galley structure.

It was a little alcove just through the wall from the galley stove and consequently it was like an oven and stank like everybody's business.

It had a steel door which opened outwards and was in two halves. The lower half could be closed to keep the sea out and the top half (if closed) would guarantee the suffocation of any occupant.

The actual 'throne' was a monstrous steel funnel or 'filler' shaped contrivance from which a discharge pipe disappeared below deck level to re-appear through the side of the ship just on the water-line.

A fousome primitive affair to be flushed out with a bucket of sea-water.

'Och aye!' says the loon again, 'It's gotten a gweed wash'!

'Ah, but!' says I, 'the richt wye, the parteeclar wye to dee't is to lean ower the side an' pit the hose up the pipe! Then ye'll be sure the pipe's clear!'

'Nivver thocht aboot that! Od! I think I'll try't,' says he.

Behold then the youngster fechtin' with the serpent hose, needing every ounce of his youth and strength to lean over the rail and thrust the hissing nozzle into the pipe. And behold the fearsome aftermath when the toilet door burst violently open and there appeared on deck an apparition which I do not desire to see again.

There stood the loon's ain father with his drawers round his ankles. His sark-tails were in a rosy knot round his neck and his bonnet had been driven forward so that the snoot now covered his nose. The pipe he had been enjoying was now emitting faint wisps of steam and to crown it all there was firmly plastered between his shoulder blades a neat square of paper from last week's *Green Final*.

From the faint watery sounds which were struggling through his clenched teeth I gathered that he was questioning the legitimacy of his own offspring who had now abandoned ship and was disappearing rapidly along the quay.

One thing has disappointed me. For the past 37 years yon loon has been convinced that I knew perfectly well that his Da was on the throne when I gave the advice on hygiene.

To think that onybody could be so ill thochtit!

In praise of the fisher's friend

'The Fisherman's Friend' is the trade-name of a particularly fiery brand of cough lozenge relished by those whose innards seem to resemble a washin'-hoose biler in consistency.

Since such a fraternity must include professional fire-eaters and tough nuts wi' hairy teeth I would ask to be counted out and I would prefer to bestow the title 'Fisherman's Friend' on something of a much more gentle nature, namely corn chaff or 'caff' as it was known to generations of fisher folk.

There was a warmth and natural friendliness about caff that modern mattresses simply cannot hope to match. Foam rubber could never produce the kindly reeshle that a caff bed produced when it was patted, a reeshle all the more endearing if one used the magic words 'Eh, I like ye!'

I'm sure that the good Lord made caff for the comfort and restoration of weary bodies and for this countless fishermen have had reason to be grateful.

Caff could be obtained in two ways. You could tak' yer caff-saick t' the fairm an' get it filled then ye wid ha'e a gey job takin' the thing hame balanced on a bike 'cos a full caff-saick's near as big as a barrage balloon.

So it wis a common sicht t' see a fisherman walkin' along a country road pushin' his bike wi' its great muckle load an' if he had a loon, the loon wid be on the ither side ready t' steady the monster.

Prood kind o' chiels wid seek the milkman t' dee the job but the milkman didna ha'e a lot o' room on his cairt so th'e cairrier sometimes got the jobbie.

Once hame the caff-saick, which was simply a huge harn (hessian) bag, was clothed in a blue cotton cover then it was ready for service.

The fisherman's blankets were spread on the kitchen floor, one on top of the other, then they were stitched together round the edges, the proper tool being a darning needle, and the materials a ball o' 5-ply navy-blue Seafield worsit.

Thus the finished 'blanket' could be as thick as individual taste dictated. Coverin' the caff-saick an' shooin'-in the blankets wis a great nicht! For the bairns, at least. A feather pillow completed the fisherman's bedding.

At the start of the herring season a clean cairt would make the rounds of the crew's homes to collect the beddin' and then came the almighty job of gettin' the stuff aboard ship.

To coax the great muckle caff-saicks through the galley door then down the ladder into the cabin and then into the bunks took a lot o' coortin' an' clappin', the unwritten law being that the cotton covers must not be dirtied or torn.

Could you have seen a bunk with its complement of fresh bedding you would have sworn that it was impossible for a human body to enter it but you would have been wrong!

The first nicht on the caff bed ye wid be near smored. Ye wid ha'e t' fecht yer wye in then lie wi' yer nose scrapin' the deck, an' the caff aneth ye reeshlin' an' squeakin' in the saick that wis fit t' burst.

The second nicht, ye wid ha'e room t' breathe but efter that the caff began t' sattle an' afore a week wis oot the 'caffer' wid be into the shape o' yersel jist like a nestie.

Oh, what comfort! Oh, what bliss! Steep broadside motion could never dislodge ye!

At the end of the year the sea around the Buchan coast bore a liberal coating of caff. Proof positive that a number of deckies were 'seekin' a shift' and had duly teemed their caff-saicks ower the side.

I often remember a beautiful spring morning in the early thirties when a certain Peterhead crew were making their way to their ship, every one of them seated on the beddin'-cairt, surrounded by rolls of blankets and great saicks o' caff.

The cairter was the kind o' chiel that wid gie onybody a shottie o' the horse for a Woodbine. In fact, for a packet o' Woodbines, ye wid get the horse to keep.

Now, Jeemsie, the young cook had been at the picters on the Setterday nicht to see Ben Hur and now he was regaling his shipmates with vivid accounts of the thrilling chariot scenes in the film.

But Jeemsie's command of descriptive language was rather limited so, sensing that he wasn't getting the message across he decided to give his pals an object lesson.

'Look!' says he. 'I'll lat ye see the wye that Ben Hur gart 'is horsie go!' Then he passed the mandatory Woodbine to the cairter and seized the reins.

'C'mon ye beast, move!' he yelled. 'Gee-up ye sod, move yer carcase! Yahoo! Yippee! Up the leg o' yer dra'ars!' while he laid into the beast's backside wi' the bicht o' the reins.

He must have touched a tender spot for the startled animal took off, 0-60 in ten seconds flat.

Oh boys! Ye nivver saw naething like yon! Jeemsie didna ken that for twa hale days the horsie had been stappin' her belly wi' lush spring grass.

Od! She wis as full o' girss as a caff-saick wis full o' caff! The sudden acceleration set off some kind of chemical reaction in the intimmers o' the horse, so that as she came thundering down Queen Street there came from her exhaust a rapid series of short, sharp bursts of warm, moist air in strict tempo with the clatter of the hooves.

There was of course an added bonus in that the unexpected zephyrs were heavily laden with rich green grass particles which were scattered liberally ower everything in the line of fire and this included Jeemsie and his pals.

Now, ony feel can gar a horsie go but it tak's a man to stop a Clydesdale, an' Jeemsie wis jist a loon! In vain did his shipmates yell 'Come astarn, for God's sake!' Jeemsie couldna stop her!

Two really brave crew-men abandoned ship in Chapel Street, another was lost overboard on the Broadgate, but the rest survived till the sweating horse came to a stop at the Brig, where Jeemsie received a few bright words from his skipper.

The cairt, the beddin' and the crew appeared as if a hunner lawn mowers had been teemed oot ower them!

Everything had to go back for washing or for clean covers and as far as I ken, Jeemsie nivver drove a horse again.

Dod just wisna the 'hale shillin'

It was six o'clock on a Saturday night in Yarmouth. Since the month was October, it was pitch dark and although almost a thousand fishing boats were tightly berthed on both sides of the long dark river, there was scarcely a glimmer of light to be seen from any one of them.

The week was finished as far as fishing was concerned and soon the streets of the East Anglian town would be in a turmoil as thousands of Scotties came ashore for Setter-day nicht.

On board the steam drifter *Wildfire* the crew were at their supper in the cabin, which was also the dining-room. Ten hungry men sat around the triangular table of whose surface scarcely an inch was visible so dense was the mass of plates, mugs and jars which covered it. Each man sat in his appointed place, near his bunk; this was standard practice.

The crew had been on the go for eighteen hours. They had hauled a fleet of herring nets containing eighty cran; on the way from the fishing ground to the river they had 'redd up' or cleaned the nets, removing all herring heads and broken fish from the meshes.

The dinner had been a joog o' tay and a pie but now that the shot had been livered and the ship washed down, the lads were enjoying a proper meal, a great dish of stewed steak with lashings of rich gravy which could be sopped up with slices of new bread. What a feed! And what a taypot! Of brown enamel it held about two gallons and it was kept continually on the move. Mair tay!

The skipper, in his fifties, was the oldest man aboard. There were three young deckies in their late teens or early twenties and all the others were married men.

Of course the 'young lads' would be off like a shot as soon as their supper wis doon their throats. They would race each other to be first for the communal bucket which was reserved for face-washing. Then, scrubbed, and dressed in their 'go-ashores', they would seek the bright lights and the lasses-o! With ten bob in his pooch a fella could have a rare weekend.

The older men would not be in such a hurry. Some of them might go ashore later for a pint at the White Lion or The Gallon Can; others might drop into the Church of Scotland Bethel to have a cup of tea and a news with old friends.

There they could receive attention to the salt-water boils on their wrists, an affliction which was the bane of their lives. The old-fashioned oilskin frocks chafed a fellas wrists, pulling hairs out by the roots and hey presto, you had a crop of 'plooks'. Very painful they were too! Most fishermen wore bandages of red flannel round their wrists to prevent the chafing. It had to be red flannel!

But sanitary conditions afloat were primitive and usually, if one man got boils, the others would be infected. Penicillin was as yet unknown and home-made cures included 'steepit loaf' or bread poultice. Some lads thought the Scriptures actually said 'Cast thy bread upon the waters and thou shalt get a steepit loaf!'

But no matter where they had spent the evening they would finish off with a baggie o' chips at the open-air stallies where you could buy mussels or shrimps or limpets or winkles. 'Gyaad-sake! Scotch folk dinna ait sic muck!'

There was one deckie, however, who was in no hurry to go ashore. Dod was a year or two younger than the skipper who counted Dod as the best hand in the crew. Experience was something that Dod had in plenty and he was a very shrewd weather forecaster; he was strictly sober and was utterly reliable but alas the poor man could neither read nor write.

He had left school with the name of 'nae bein' the 'hale shillin' ' but then his generation had never heard of dyslexia, just as they had never heard of antibiotics or television.

Tonight Dod would sit until everybody had gone ashore, leaving him alone with the skipper. Then Dod would produce the letter he had received that day from his faithful Annie who always posted the letter so that Dod would get it on Saturday.

The letter, unopened, would be handed to the skipper who would ceremoniously open it before reading its contents aloud to the eager listener. Such had been their custom for many seasons!

But this particular evening the skipper laid the open letter on the table and addressed Dod very earnestly:

'Dod! I dinna like this! Here's me readin' a letter that's supposed to be private! Man, I hiv to look at it, an' I canna help hearin' ivvery word that Annie has to say! Fit wye can that be private? The letter's meant for you yersel'!'

For a moment Dod sat in silence, then reaching across the table he clappit his twa han's ower the skipper's lugs and said triumphantly 'It's private noo, Skipper! Read awa'!'

Nae the hale shillin'?